GREAT MORNING!
Poems for School Leaders to Read Aloud

POETRY ANTHOLOGIES
BY VARDELL & WONG

THE POETRY FRIDAY ANTHOLOGY
Teacher Edition (Grades K-5)
Common Core version or TEKS version

THE POETRY FRIDAY ANTHOLOGY FOR MIDDLE SCHOOL
Teacher Edition (Grades 6-8)
Common Core version or TEKS version

THE POETRY FRIDAY ANTHOLOGY FOR SCIENCE
Teacher/Librarian Edition (K-5)
with an optional Supplemental TEKS Guide
Student Edition (The Poetry of Science)

THE POETRY FRIDAY ANTHOLOGY FOR CELEBRATIONS
Teacher/Librarian Edition
Student Edition

THE POETRY FRIDAY POWER BOOK SERIES
YOU JUST WAIT (tweens + teens)
HERE WE GO (Grades 3 + up)
PET CRAZY (Grades K-4)

GREAT MORNING!

Poems for School Leaders to Read Aloud

BY THE CREATORS OF THE POETRY FRIDAY ANTHOLOGY® SERIES

SYLVIA VARDELL & JANET WONG

PomeloBooks.com

This book is dedicated to our mothers:
Ingrid Mergeler
Joyce Wong

Pomelo Books
4580 Province Line Road
Princeton, NJ 08540
www.PomeloBooks.com
info@PomeloBooks.com

Library of Congress Cataloging-in-Publication Data is available.

ISBN 978-1-937057-28-2

Please visit us:
www.PomeloBooks.com

POETS

Alma Flor Ada

Brod Bagert

Michelle Heidenrich Barnes

Robyn Hood Black

Susan Blackaby

Merry Bradshaw

Lydia Breiseth

Joseph Bruchac

Kate Coombs

Cynthia Cotten

Kristy Dempsey

Margarita Engle

Janet Clare Fagal

Catherine Flynn

Xelena González

Joan Bransfield Graham

Lorie Ann Grover

Mary Lee Hahn

Avis Harley

Jane Heitman Healy

Sara Holbrook

Ann Ingalls

Julie Larios

Renée M. LaTulippe

B.J. Lee

Suzy Levinson

Elaine Magliaro

Kenn Nesbitt

Eric Ode

Linda Sue Park

Ann Whitford Paul

Greg Pincus

Jack Prelutsky

Bob Raczka

Heidi Bee Roemer

Caroline Starr Rose

Laura Purdie Salas

Michael Salinger

Darren Sardelli

Liz Garton Scanlon

Michelle Schaub

Laura Shovan

Buffy Silverman

Eileen Spinelli

Traci Sorell

Elizabeth Steinglass

Holly Thompson

Linda Kulp Trout

Amy Ludwig VanDerwater

Carol Varsalona

April Halprin Wayland

Carole Boston Weatherford

Kay Winters

Allan Wolf

Virginia Euwer Wolff

Janet Wong

Jane Yolen

TABLE OF CONTENTS

WHY POETRY?

When we think about what poetry does for children—and in just a few minutes of sharing on a regular basis—it's a pretty impressive list. Author and literacy expert Mem Fox noted, "Rhymers will be readers; it's that simple." Here are some key benefits of sharing poetry with children:

WHY POETRY?

Poetry reinforces word sounds, rhymes, patterns & pronunciation.

Poetry is rich in imagery that stimulates the imagination.

Poetry introduces new vocabulary & figurative language.

Poetry offers an emotional connection & affirmation.

Poetry enriches the curriculum, captures concepts & builds content.

Poetry provides practice for building listening & comprehension.

Poetry is accessible to a wide range of reading abilities & language learning skill levels.

Poetry can be revisited again & again, with different responses at different ages & stages.

Poetry makes you smarter . . . all kinds of research indicates that rhyme, rhythm, and imagery boost memory formation and recall.
Rebecca Rupp

POETRY FRIDAY

In many classrooms and libraries, the concept of **Poetry Friday** is thriving, with teachers and librarians spending five minutes to share a poem and connect it with children's lives. Pausing to share a poem on Poetry Friday—and to reinforce a language arts or social studies or science skill—is an easy way to infuse poetry into our teaching practices.

Why not bring the Poetry Friday concept into your morning announcements, taking just a minute every Friday to share a poem? Readers of these morning announcement poems could include the principal, office staff, nurse, counselor, custodian, security guard or police officer, parent volunteers, guest readers from the community, and student leaders. Have fun creating your school's reading rituals on Poetry Fridays— and on any day. And don't be surprised if it's a wonderful poem moment that students remember most vividly at the end of the school year!

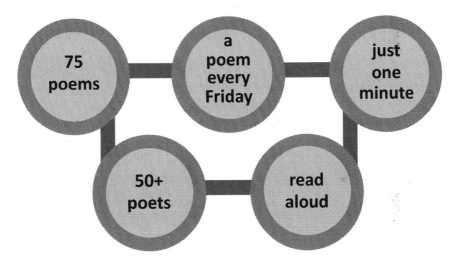

We offer a set of 36 poems—**a poem-a-week for the nine months of the typical school year**—to start the day, along with a linked poem for each featured poem on the same topic, plus bonus poems to start and end the year, for **a total of 75 poems. You'll find new poems by more than 50+ contemporary poets** who write for young people, as well as some favorites reprinted from our Poetry Friday books. Our goal is to provide support for those who might be unfamiliar with today's poetry for young people and might need guidance in how to begin.

A guiding principle of this book is that **poetry is meant to be read aloud**. Like song lyrics that sit quietly on the page, the music of poetry comes alive when spoken and shared. Whether you introduce a poem at the beginning of the day, when transitioning to lunch or a break, or when wrapping things up for the day, "breaking" for poetry provides a moment to refresh and engage with language, ideas, and each other.

IN THIS BOOK

The poems in this book are arranged to echo the usual rhythm of the school year, but **feel free to share any and all of the poems with students any time, in any order, and in any way you like.**

You can **use the Subject Index** (on pages 162-163) **to find a particular poem** for a special occasion or need. We also provide a simple prompt to read BEFORE reading the poem aloud to set the stage with intriguing facts related to the poem. Plus, you'll find a brief comment to follow up the poem—all prepared for you and ready to share in just a minute or two. If time allows, you can read a second poem linked to the featured poem, too.

You might also encourage teachers to share the day's poem again in their classrooms. **We even offer Hidden Language Skills (pages 139-143) that teachers can incorporate into their lesson plans,** as appropriate. And you can use the Letter to Parents (page 158) with the Sharing Poetry at Home idea sheet (page 159) to bring parents on board. The more children hear, read, say, and experience the poem, the more they internalize the sounds, words, and meanings of the poem and begin to notice the mechanics and artistry of poetry.

POETRY SHARING TIPS

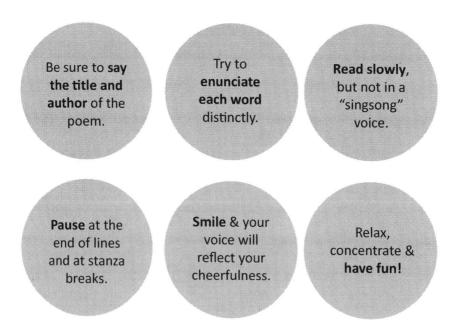

Be sure to **say the title and author** of the poem.

Try to **enunciate each word** distinctly.

Read slowly, but not in a "singsong" voice.

Pause at the end of lines and at stanza breaks.

Smile & your voice will reflect your cheerfulness.

Relax, concentrate & **have fun!**

HOW TO USE THIS BOOK

1
Read aloud the **"DID YOU KNOW"** intro.

2
Read aloud the **featured poem**.

3
Read aloud the **"FOLLOW UP"** invitation.

4
If time allows, read aloud the **"CONNECT"** linked poem.

DID YOU KNOW?

Did you know that there are different ways people greet each other in different countries? They stick out their tongues in Tibet and clap their hands rhythmically in Shona ethnic groups in southern Africa. The fist bump may have started in the United States among motorcyclists in the 1940s.

Here's a poem to get our morning started today.

GREAT MORNING!
by Janet Wong

Good morning, everybody!
Get set to learn and study!

GREAT morning, everyone!
Get set to have some FUN!

FOLLOW UP

Ready to learn?
And study?
And have fun?
Make it a GREAT morning.
It's up to you!

CONNECT

For another poem celebrating TODAY, link with "The Most Glad-to-See Day of the Year" by Allan Wolf (page 127).

TO HANDLE YOURSELF,
USE YOUR HEAD;
TO HANDLE OTHERS,
USE YOUR HEART.

ELEANOR ROOSEVELT

POEMS

POETRY FRIDAYS

by Janet Wong

Poetry Mondays make us mindful,
calm us down, help us see.

Poetry Tuesdays tell our stories.
Let's write poems . . . starring *me!*

Wednesdays are for poems and art.
Words plus pictures make us smart.

On Poetry Thursdays we do STEM.
Poet? Scientist? We're both of them!

But of all the days, Friday is king.
Poetry Fridays are EVERYTHING!

DID YOU KNOW?

Did you know that people greet each other in different ways in different countries? They stick out their tongues in Tibet and clap their hands rhythmically in Shona ethnic groups in southern Africa. The fist bump may have started in the United States among motorcyclists in the 1940s. Here's a poem to get our morning started today.

FOLLOW UP

Ready to learn?
And study?
And have fun?
Make it a GREAT morning.
It's up to you!

CONNECT

For another poem celebrating TODAY, link with "The Most Glad-to-See Day of the Year" by Allan Wolf (page 127).

POETRY PLUS
Also share this poem on field trip days or when guest speakers come.

GREAT MORNING!
by Janet Wong

Good morning, everybody!
Get set to learn and study!

GREAT morning, everyone!
Get set to have some FUN!

DID YOU KNOW?

Your parents, guardians, and family are also part of our school team. We count on them to help and support you as you keep learning 24 hours a day, 7 days a week. So it's very important that we share our school news with them at home. This next poem helps us remember that, and we hope it helps YOU remember to take home school forms and bring them back again, too.

FOLLOW UP

When those forms go home with you, please share them and bring them back again—signed and soon.

CONNECT

For another poem about school forms, link with the thoughtful and serious poem "Who Am I?" by Margarita Engle (page 105).

POETRY PLUS
Also share this poem to remind students about important paperwork all year long.

OH, THOSE FORMS!

by Janet Clare Fagal

School forms are quite important—
they're filled with things to do.
Be sure your family checks them
to learn about our news.

Don't forget the book fair—
be sure to bring your money!
Menus for another month,
picnic plans for when it's sunny!
Sign-ups for an instrument,
try-outs for the play,
what to bring on field trips,
and Visiting Author Day!
Reminders from the office,
forms the nurse will need,
parent-conference planning,
great new books to read!

ALL forms are quite important—
they're filled with things for you!
So be sure your family reads them
to hear about school news!

Poem copyright © 2018 by Janet Clare Fagal
from *GREAT Morning! Poems for School Leaders to Read Aloud*
by Sylvia Vardell & Janet Wong (Pomelo Books)

DID YOU KNOW?

In times of an emergency, crisis, or disaster, most people become very emotional rather than thoughtful. But in an emergency, the most important thing to do is stay calm. That's why we need to practice what to do BEFORE an emergency actually occurs. Like getting ready for a sports game, your brain will perform best if you put it through a few practice sessions. Here's a poem to remind us about getting ready and staying safe.

FOLLOW UP

Being ready for an emergency means practicing drills, learning safety skills, thinking fast, staying alert, and acting smart. That way, if trouble comes, no one will be hurt.

CONNECT

When it's also time to focus on a fire safety plan, link with "Beep, Beep, Beep!" by Suzy Levinson (page 114).

POETRY PLUS
Also share this poem after safety drills & preparations.

WE'LL KEEP SAFE

by Janet Wong

We're getting ready.
We're practicing drills.
We're learning
our safety skills.

We're thinking fast.
We're acting smart.
We're learning
how to do our part.

We're keeping safe.
We're staying alert.
If trouble comes,
we won't be hurt.

DID YOU KNOW?

Did you know that people have been using the term "single file" for nearly 500 years? The idea of lining up one behind the other has been useful for describing animals, things, and people for a long, long time. Today, we'll share a poem about lining up "single file" for lunch every day.

FOLLOW UP

When you line up today, think about using "silent feet" just like in this poem:
"Single file. Silent feet."
I'll see you in the hallways, and I hope I only hear "silent feet"!

CONNECT

There are so many rules for students to internalize as they grow up. Link with "Things Not to Do" by Eileen Spinelli (page 123) for a humorous and truthful look at good manners and etiquette.

POETRY PLUS

Also share this poem during or prior to lunchtime.

TIME FOR LUNCH

by Caroline Starr Rose

Everyone, please form a line.
Single file. Silent feet.
Who can show the quiet sign?
Everyone, please form a line.
To the lunchroom just in time.
Find a bench. Dig on in.
Keep your table nice and neat.
Everyone, please form a line.
Single file. Silent feet.

DID YOU KNOW?

How many languages are there all around the world? No one really knows. But within the United States alone, more than 350 different languages are spoken today. This poem reminds us that even if you don't speak 350 languages, everyone understands the language of the **smile**.

Pronunciation Guide
Aloha (uh- **low**- ha)
Ciao (chow)
Hola (**oh** - la)
Salut (sah - **loo)**
Goddag (goo - **day**)
Shalom (shah - **loam**)

FOLLOW UP

This poem includes greetings in seven different languages: English (*Hello*), Hawaiian (*Aloha*), Italian (*Ciao*), Spanish (*Hola*), French (*Salut*), Danish (*Goddag*), and Hebrew (*Shalom*). Try greeting someone in one of these languages OTHER than English during the day today!

CONNECT

For another poem about the benefits of speaking more than one language, link with "Bilingual"/ "Bilingüe" by Alma Flor Ada (pages 97, 98).

Topic 4: Inclusion

POETRY PLUS
Also share this poem during Random Acts of Kindness Week in February.

HOW TO MAKE A FRIEND

by Jane Heitman Healy

You start by saying *Hi there,*
Hello, Aloha, Ciao—
If someone answers back to you,
Smile and nod and bow.

You might try saying *Hola,*
Salut, Goddag, Shalom.
If someone answers back to you,
They might be far from home.

A friend begins by greeting
Those they meet along the way
To make them feel welcome
At home, at school, at play.

DID YOU KNOW?

Did you know that the first photograph made with a camera was taken nearly 200 years ago? A man in France took a picture out his window. Today, most people use their cell phones to take photographs, and more than a trillion digital pictures are taken each year worldwide. Do you say "cheese" when you get your photo taken? This poem wonders why . . .

FOLLOW UP

Think about surprising your friends and family the next time someone takes a photograph by saying "FLEAS!" instead of "cheese!"

CONNECT

For a fun and silly poem about taking a photograph of yourself (the "selfie"), look for the linked poem "Selfie" by Lorie Ann Grover (page 107).

POETRY PLUS
Also share this poem for picture day, special programs, Open House, recitals, etc.

PHOTO OP

by Linda Sue Park

"Get together, look this way.
Lean in—you'll have to squeeze.
That's it—that's good, just stay right there.
And one-two-three—say CHEESE!"

Can someone tell me why it is
we have to holler "cheese"?
Just once I'd like a photo snapped
while everyone yells "FLEAS!"

DID YOU KNOW?

Have you ever played a matching game? You put two things together because they have something in common. For example, you can look at a list of words and match the pairs of words that go together. This is great for what is called "brain training," helping us use our brains to keep them active and growing. In this poem, listen carefully for the pairs of words that go together.

FOLLOW UP

Think about the foods you like. Would you include any of the foods in this poem—like pizza, liver, zucchini, tomatoes, potatoes, oatmeal, or ice cream? Stretch your brain and think of your favorite food and what you might compare it to.

CONNECT

When it's time for lunch, the focus is not only on food, but on time with friends too. Link this poem with "Lunchtime" by Janet Wong (page 132) to highlight both these aspects of lunchtime for students.

POETRY PLUS
Also share this poem during school breakfast or after-school care.

FOOD FEST

by Heidi Bee Roemer

Chef is to restaurant as teacher is to school.
Stove is to hot as fridge is to cool.

Milk is to drink as egg is to eat.
Lemon is to sour as sugar is to sweet.

Oatmeal is to breakfast as sandwich is to lunch.
Soup is to slurp as carrot is to crunch.

Steak is to chew as shakes are to sip.
Cone is to ice cream as chips are to dip.

Ears are to corn as eyes are to potatoes.
Green is to zucchini as red is to tomatoes.

Fuel is to car as food is to tummy.
Liver is to yucky as pizza is to yummy!

Poem copyright © 2013 by Heidi Bee Roemer
GREAT Morning! Poems for School Leaders to Read Aloud
by Sylvia Vardell & Janet Wong (Pomelo Books)

DID YOU KNOW?

The first school nurse in the U.S. cared for 10,000 students in four New York schools back in 1902. It was an experiment that worked, and today there are nearly 100,000 nurses working in schools across the country. The next poem reminds us how nurses can help us when we don't feel so well.

[In the final stanza of this poem, insert the name of your school nurse or the person children should seek out when they're not feeling well.]

FOLLOW UP

Nurses take care of us whether at school, in a clinic, at a doctor's office, or in the hospital. Thank goodness for nurses!

CONNECT

For a poem about who takes care of the nurse when he or she is sick, link with "I Wonder Who" by Eric Ode (page 116).

POETRY PLUS
Also share this poem during flu season and on School Nurse Day in May.

SCHOOL NURSE

by Elizabeth Steinglass

If you slip
and scrape your shin,

if your snack
wants out, not in,

if your eyes
get gooey and pink,

if your head's
too hot to think.

What should you do?
Where should you go?

Find Nurse _____ .
S/he will know.

Poem copyright © 2018 by Elizabeth Steinglass
from *GREAT Morning! Poems for School Leaders to Read Aloud*
by Sylvia Vardell & Janet Wong (Pomelo Books)

DID YOU KNOW?

When she was a little girl, Clara Barton took care of her brother when he was sick. Many years later, she worked as a nurse during the Civil War, and then established the American Red Cross in 1881 to help people in times of need. This next poem is about helping others like the Red Cross does all over the world.

FOLLOW UP

The next time you read about an emergency on the news or see a friend in need nearby—even right here at our school—think about how you can be a helper too, a person who cares.

CONNECT

If you're not sure about when and where to help, this linked poem, "If You See Something, Say Something" by Janet Wong (page 130), provides good advice.

POETRY PLUS

Also share this poem during times of crisis and emergency in the community.

LOOK FOR THE HELPERS

by Michelle Heidenrich Barnes

Look for the helpers
The healers
The givers

The arms-open
Hand-holding
Everyday heroes

The ones who bring food
Extra clothes
And first aid

Who offer safe shelter
A roof
And a bed

Follow their lead
Be a hugger
A helper

A friend who will listen
A person
Who cares

DID YOU KNOW?

Did you know that in some schools, special guests like business and community leaders get to be the "principal for a day"? Sometimes even students get to participate! They don't really take over the whole job, but they do help with announcements, meetings, lunches, buses, and other duties. In the next poem, we can imagine what it might be like if a principal and a student switched places completely.

FOLLOW UP

What might happen when we switch places with someone else? We might begin to see the world through their eyes. Think about that the next time you disagree with someone or don't understand their point of view.

CONNECT

For a poem about "each person looking out for each other," share this linked poem, "Let's Pledge Between Us" by Janet Wong (page 131).

POETRY PLUS
Also share this poem on School Principals' Day on May 1.

PRINCIPAL FOR A DAY

by Laura Shovan

Today
a kid
gets to be
the principal!

The principal
gets to be
a kid
today.

Note: This is a "reverso" poem
(see Hidden Language Skills, page 143).

DID YOU KNOW?

The word "grade" comes from the French word "grade" and the Latin word "gradus," meaning a step that you climb—like on a stair. We only started around 1886 to use the word "grade" to mean a letter mark or a number score for a student's work. So let's think of report card grades as steps in a student's learning!

FOLLOW UP

When you get your report card, remember it might not "show your favorite features," but you can always keep working on being your very best self!

CONNECT

There are many ways we share our successes and build good attitudes. With the poem "Compliment Chain" by Mary Lee Hahn (page 108), we can show students how to give each other positive feedback.

Topic 10: Feedback

POETRY PLUS

Also share this poem every time there are report cards or parent conferences.

REPORT CARDS

by Janet Wong

A report card is like a photo.
It might capture you perfectly.
Or it might look very wrong to you.
You might not like what you see.

If your report card happens not
to show your favorite features,
next time make sure you show
your best self to your teachers!

DID YOU KNOW?

There are more than two million people across the United States who keep our schools running, but who are NOT teachers, librarians, or principals. Yes, schools can't run without wonderful secretaries, cafeteria staff, clerks, custodians, and more. In this poem, we pause to thank those people for making our school such a special place.

FOLLOW UP

Next time you see a school staff member who helps with buses, answers questions, makes phone calls, and handles all kinds of issues here at school, be sure to say THANK YOU!

CONNECT

One of the most under-appreciated school staff members may be the school custodian. Link with "Our Custodian" by Ann Ingalls (page 110) to highlight the contributions of this important staff member.

POETRY PLUS

Also share this poem on staff member birthdays.

TO OUR FRONT OFFICE STAFF: A CELEBRATION

by Kay Winters

You deal with the issues

    each school day brings.

      Bells sound

        Buzzers buzz

          Questions fly

            The phone rings

        Buses come

      Buses go

    Late start

Too *many* things!

  You work your magic,

    without any fuss.

      So here's a BIG THANK YOU—

        from all of us.

DID YOU KNOW?

Did you know that "hooray" is an exclamation that comes from the word "huzza" used way back in 1573? We use exclamation words like "hooray," "yippee," "yahoo," and "woo hoo" to express joy, approval, or encouragement. The next poem uses the word "hooray" over and over again to celebrate all kinds of kids.

FOLLOW UP

Do you love words? Birds? Rocks? Building? Singing? Drawing? Counting? And standing up for what is fair? Hooray for all the kids at our school today!

CONNECT

For another poem that celebrates all kinds of kids, link with "Friends" by Renée M. LaTulippe (page 112).

POETRY PLUS

Also share this poem to celebrate student accomplishments of all kinds all year long.

ALL KINDS OF KIDS

by Elizabeth Steinglass

Hooray for the kids who love using words!
Hooray for the kids who chatter with birds!

Hooray for the kids who identify rocks!
Hooray for the kids who build bridges with blocks!

Hooray for the kids who sing to the stars!
Hooray for the kids who draw cats driving cars!

Hooray for the kids who count every stair!
Hooray for the kids who speak up for what's fair!

Hooray for all kinds of kids.

DID YOU KNOW?

There are many ways to get to school. Most kids arrive by bus, car, bicycle, and walking. In Tokyo, many students take the subway to school; in Nepal, some students paddle to school in a kayak; and in Caracas, Venezuela, they may board a gondola cable car to go to school! No matter how you travel to school, the next poem reminds us that feeling safe is our number one priority.

FOLLOW UP

When you come to school or head home after school, remember three things: be kind to your fellow travelers; stay safe; and if there's ever a problem, let me or another caring grown-up know right away.

CONNECT

To celebrate the freedom kids feel when riding a bike, link with the poem "Bicycle Dreams" by Michael Salinger (page 119).

ON YOUR WAY TO SCHOOL
by Laura Purdie Salas

POETRY PLUS
Also share this poem during School Bus Safety Week or Walk to School Day in October.

By bus,
by bike,
by car,
on foot,
you came to school today.

In boots
or sandals,
sun
or rain—
we're glad you made your way.

Shared laughs
or whispers,
jokes,
good news . . .
we hope that's what you heard.

Did drivers,
classmates,
neighbors,
friends
each share a kindly word?

We hope no stranger stood too close
and made you feel uneasy,
and nobody said anything
that left you feeling queasy.

Are you feeling scared or nervous?
Not sure what to do?
Our safety team will listen.
Brainstorm.
We'll look out for you!

DID YOU KNOW?

Did you know that 62 million people across the country volunteered their time to help others this year? The families at our school are part of that big number! Here is a poem that reminds us of how we can count on them to attend our sporting events and special programs; help with book fairs, bake sales, and fundraising; and keep us going at home and at school.

FOLLOW UP

Be sure to tell your parents, grandparents, uncles, aunts, and friends they are #1 and A++ at our school!

CONNECT

For a poem that is also a letter of thanks, link with "Sincerely" by Robyn Hood Black (page 99).

POETRY PLUS
Also share this poem any time there are special events for school families.

#1 AND A++

by Janet Wong

Bake sale? Book fair?
Fundraising plans?
Our families are
our faithful fans.

Parents, grandparents,
uncles, aunts, friends—
all day, all night,
and on weekends—

You are the ones
who keep us on track
by volunteering.
You have our backs.

We're grateful
for all you do for us.
You're #1.
You're A++!

DID YOU KNOW?

A famous cartoonist, Lynn Johnston, once said, "An apology is the superglue of life. It can repair just about anything." Saying sorry isn't easy, but it's an important part of admitting that we have made a mistake or we have hurt someone in some way. This next poem shows us how saying sorry can be hard, but can also be so helpful and healing.

FOLLOW UP

The next time you find you did something you shouldn't have—or said something you wish you hadn't—muster your courage and say you're sorry.

CONNECT

For a different perspective on dealing with feelings, link with "Poem for a Bully" by Eileen Spinelli (page 122).

POETRY PLUS
Also share this poem during times of conflict or tension.

SCARY TERRITORY

by Janet Wong

It can be scary
saying sorry—
will or won't they
believe your story?
And, of course,
you're going to worry
if saying sorry works.

Saying sorry
takes some courage.
Saying sorry
takes some guts.
It definitely isn't fun
to sit down and discuss
how you should've
acted,
what you could've
said—
but
this very scary territory
is mainly in your head!

DID YOU KNOW?

We celebrate a new year every January, but we also celebrate another new beginning when we start school every year. Did you know there is a new year celebration somewhere in the world every single month? For example, there is the Buddhist celebration of Songkran every April in Thailand; Matariki, the Maori New Year, in New Zealand in June; and Ethiopians greet the new year at Enkutatash in September. Here's a poem to celebrate the new year whenever it occurs.

FOLLOW UP

Start your new year TODAY with new dreams, goals, plans, paths, skills, hopes, cares, and facts to know. Every day is another opportunity to start fresh.

CONNECT

For another poem that is all about learning NEW SKILLS, link with "What We're Learning" by Janet Wong (page 135).

Topic 16: A Fresh Start

POETRY PLUS
Also share this poem as the new calendar year begins or for ANY new year celebration.

NEW YEAR IS HERE

by Kenn Nesbitt

New Year is here!
Let's shout.
Let's cheer!
Yippee! Yahoo!
We start anew.
New dreams to chase.
New goals to face.
New plans to make.
New paths to take.
New skills to learn.
New stars to earn.
New hopes.
New prayers.
New loves.
New cares.
New facts to know.
Can't wait. Let's go!
Let's shout!
Let's cheer!
It's here! New Year!

DID YOU KNOW?

Did you know not everyone celebrates their birthdays on the day they were born? Some people don't celebrate birthdays at all. And in some countries like Vietnam, the tradition is for everyone to celebrate their birthday together on New Year's Day. The following poem is for anyone celebrating a birthday today—or any day!

FOLLOW UP

Whatever your birthday and however you celebrate (or don't celebrate), YOU are a gift to this school. Each one of you is special and unique and like no one else.

CONNECT

For a look at how some Native American tribes count birthdays, link with "Winter Counting" by Joseph Bruchac (page 102).

Topic 17: Birthdays

POETRY PLUS
Also share this poem for a special birthday for a staff member or student.

WHEN YOU ARRIVED: A BIRTHDAY POEM

by Liz Garton Scanlon

When you arrived
you were given a gift—
your own day
your own square
on the calendar
that would forever
be your birthday!

When you arrived
you were given a gift—
your very own day.
Yes, you were given a gift
when you arrived,
and so were we.
Happy birthday!

DID YOU KNOW?

Experts have found that spending time outside can help us feel more peaceful. But it's not always possible to go outside. What are some other things we can do to reduce stress? Listen carefully: this next poem will remind us of some things you can do during outdoor or indoor recess.

FOLLOW UP

Whether you're running or reading or drawing or talking, taking a break will reboot your brain so you can come back to class ready to focus and work.

CONNECT

Link with the poem "Time for School" by Ann Whitford Paul (page 117) for another look at class time and recess time.

POETRY PLUS
Also share this poem for Yoga-Recess Day in February or Physical Fitness Month in May.

RECESS

by Avis Harley

Some play soccer,
some run races.
Others read
in quiet places.

Some find leaves
or draw with chalk.
Some play tag,
while others talk.

A few play chess.
Lots play ball.
And some just like
to watch it all.

Poem copyright © 2012 by Avis Harley
GREAT Morning! Poems for School Leaders to Read Aloud
by Sylvia Vardell & Janet Wong (Pomelo Books)

DID YOU KNOW?

Did you know that even 20 minutes of walking every day will help your brain function better? Researchers have found that students who participate in physical activity are 20% more likely to earn an A in math or English. Listen to how this poem describes many ways we can build our bodies and our brains in gym class.

FOLLOW UP

Thanks to our teachers in gym and physical education, we have the opportunity to exercise our bodies AND our brains. Think about that the next time you go to gym class or take a walk.

CONNECT

To energize the students (and faculty and staff), link with "Let's Go" by Merry Bradshaw (page 100).

Topic 19: Physical Education

POETRY PLUS
Also share this poem during National Physical Fitness Month in May.

GYM TEACHERS
by Darren Sardelli

The gym teachers teach us the rules of each game.
They tell us to treat everybody the same.
They show us the right way to dribble a ball—
encouraging students to give it their all.

There's so many things that we're taught in this class—
kicking a soccer ball, learning to pass,
serving a volleyball, stretching each muscle,
how to do push-ups, run relays, and hustle.

We're thankful for all of the sit-ups we do,
their tips on nutrition, and key points of view.
These uplifting teachers are noble as knights—
supporting our dreams as we climb to new heights.

DID YOU KNOW?

Did you know there are more than four million school teachers across the U.S.? They get up early, take care of their own families, and spend the day here at school helping you learn and grow. Then, back at home at night and on weekends, they write lesson plans and grade papers and tests. What keeps them motivated? STUDENTS! This next poem reminds us of this important fact.

FOLLOW UP

Think about all the teachers who have helped you ace that test and do your best. They want you to feel good about *you!*

CONNECT

Who else works hard to help students learn? Substitute teachers! Share the linked poem "In the Life of a Substitute" by Lydia Breiseth (page 101).

POETRY PLUS
Also share this poem during National Teacher Appreciation Week in May.

YOUR TEACHER

by Joseph Bruchac

Your teacher
Wants you to ace that test.

Your teacher
Wants you to do your best.

Whether it's Reading
or Science or Math
your teacher
always wants you to pass.

But what your teacher
wants most, it's true,
is for you to feel
good about you.

Poem copyright © 2018 by Joseph Bruchac
from *GREAT Morning! Poems for School Leaders to Read Aloud*
by Sylvia Vardell & Janet Wong (Pomelo Books)

DID YOU KNOW?

What is the most frequently used letter in the English language? **E.** What is the most frequently used word? If you guessed "**the**," you're right! We learn to read, spell, and decode about 40,000 words as we grow up. And who can help us build vocabulary and fine-tune our reading skills at school? The reading specialist—the focus of our next poem.

FOLLOW UP

As you read in class today, think about how you are also learning to "untangle new words, discover connections, and make meaning, too." Keep reading in school and after school every day!

CONNECT

For a poem about how reading can be a passageway to take us far away, link with "Secret Worlds" by Margarita Engle (page 104).

POETRY PLUS
Also share this poem on Read Across America Day on March 2.

WHAT DOES A READING SPECIALIST DO?

by Linda Kulp Trout

Like a detective,
a reading specialist
gathers clues—
listening
as you read—
then figures out
the skills you need.

A reading specialist
shows you how
to untangle new words,
discover connections,
and make meaning, too.

Helping children
learn to read—
that's what
reading specialists do.

DID YOU KNOW?

The famous artist Picasso once said, "Every child is an artist; the problem is staying an artist when you grow up." Being creative can mean drawing or painting, making or building things, taking photographs, or even using digital technology. This next poem celebrates many ways to be artistic and creative.

FOLLOW UP

Expressing yourself through art is not just fun, but it helps your brain grow and boosts your self-esteem, too. Take the time to try many different ways of being creative and see which you enjoy most.

CONNECT

For a look at the many creative ways we can use green screen videos, link with "Virtual Adventure" by Renée M. LaTulippe (page 113).

POETRY PLUS
Also share this poem during Youth Art Month, usually celebrated in March.

ART CLASS

by Carol Varsalona

Bright open space
Tables not in rows
Supplies in jars
Work displayed for shows
Green screen ready
Artists lining up
Camera flashing
Our creative hub

DID YOU KNOW?

Did you know that when we sing or play a musical instrument, we're growing smarter? Researchers found that children who actively participate in music class showed large improvements in how the brain processes speech and reading. Making music helps our brains tackle higher level tasks. Today's poem presents several ways to get involved with music and musical instruments.

FOLLOW UP

This poem mentions so many different ways to make music, like playing the banjo, the drum, maracas, sticks, guitars, and even kazoos. We might not have all those instruments at this school, but we can all do like the poem says and sing a song!

CONNECT

Link with a poem about what it feels like to perform in a choir recital: "My Kindergarten Choir" by Avis Harley (page 109).

POETRY PLUS
Also share this poem during Music In Our Schools Month in March.

MAKE A JOYFUL NOISE

by B.J. Lee

Pick on a banjo.
Bang on a drum.
What sound does it make?
Rum-tum-tum.

Shake some maracas.
Clack some sticks.
Grab your guitar
and play some licks.

Open your mouth
and sing a song,
or toot your kazoo
the whole day long.

DID YOU KNOW?

Have you ever wondered what makes apps, smartphones, laptops, and video games work? It's coding—how computer programmers communicate with these digital devices to make them work. And learning to code is an essential part of the STEM jobs of the future. Here's a poem that shows the fun behind coding.

FOLLOW UP

This poem shows us the creativity and problem solving behind computer coding. The next time you tap an app on a cell phone or tablet, think about who created that app—maybe that's something you can learn to do, too!

CONNECT

For another poem about problem solving with technology, link with "Tech Today" by Holly Thompson (page 124).

POETRY PLUS

Also share this poem for Computer Science Education Week in December.

CAT CODER

by Buffy Silverman

Create a game.
Set up a scene
where cats can dance
across your screen.

Step-by-step,
you'll plan, you'll test
to find the path
that works the best.

A computer needs
directions, too.
Your code will tell it
what to do.

Move ten steps.
Turn right then stop.
Loop four times.
Add a drumbeat bop.

With your code
your cats sashay.
Share your game.
Let others play.

Note: This poem is loosely built around Scratch, a program that helps girls and boys learn to code. Visit https://scratch.mit.edu for more info.

DID YOU KNOW?

Did you know that there are young people who have made amazing scientific discoveries? For example, ten-year-old Kathryn Gray is the youngest person to discover a supernova. Thirteen-year-old Larry Caduada found a substance in celery that is a safer coolant than Freon. Nearly 10 million students in grades K-12 participate in science fairs every year—maybe many of you are future scientists! Listen for the surprise ending in this silly science poem.

FOLLOW UP

Sometimes science means vinegar volcanoes and hamster mazes, and sometimes science means ribbons and trophies. But most of the time, science means wondering, questioning, observing, and investigating—over and over again.

CONNECT

For many more examples of what science includes, link with "What Is Science?" by Cynthia Cotten (page 103).

POETRY PLUS
Also share this poem for STEM-STEAM on November 8 & during the science fair.

SCIENCE FAIR

by Eric Ode

I thought I'd win a ribbon
and my work would be rewarded.
My research, clearly catalogued,
my variables, recorded;
I proudly set my project
with the other kids' displays—
the vinegar volcanoes
and the cardboard hamster maze.
I waited for my trophy,
feeling confident and grand.
And that's about the time
when things got slightly out of hand.
Now my teacher's looking troubled,
and I bet she's holding grudges.
My project ate my tri-fold
and then seven of the judges.

DID YOU KNOW?

People love to laugh at jokes, don't they?
"Did you hear the one about the bed?"
[pause]
"It hasn't been made up yet!"
[pause]
Now here's a poem that has a joke built in.

FOLLOW UP

April Fools' Day can be a fun time for silly riddles and practical jokes, as long as nobody gets hurt. So we're not going to throw footballs down the hall or make phone calls in class, but you can use your brain to tell a joke or make a pun or create a silly song.

CONNECT

Link this with another poem about sharing riddles, jokes, and silly stories: "No Kidding" by Michelle Schaub (page 120).

POETRY PLUS

Also share this poem on April Fools' Day (April 1) or Tell a Joke Day in August.

TODAY'S THE DAY

by Greg Pincus

Just kick back—don't use your brains.
Turn your papers into planes.
Throw a football down the hall.
Phones in class? Sure! Make a call.
Tell the world we don't need schools!
And one more thing—April Fools.

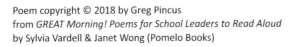

DID YOU KNOW?

Did you know that the average public library has over 100,000 books? The largest libraries in this country have millions of books—plus computers, audio books, videos, and even some surprising items. Examples of unusual things that you can borrow from public libraries are: animal skeletons (at a library in Alaska), sleds (at a library in Maine), cake pans (at a library in Iowa), prom dresses (at a library in Texas), and even Santa suits (at a library in Mississippi)!

FOLLOW UP

What do you want to learn more about? Stars? Cars? Hammerhead sharks? Look for a book that interests you in the library this week!

CONNECT

To further emphasize the importance of the school library, link with "Thankful" by Traci Sorell (page 121).

THE LIBRARY
by Sara Holbrook

POETRY PLUS
Also share this poem during National Library Week in April.

Take the walk
to the open door,
this is where you
find out more
about the stars,
oceans, quakes,
dragons, cars,
cheetahs, snakes,
unicorns, and
jumping beans,
horses, bugs,
and time machines.
From killer whales,
and free-tailed bats,
to hammerheads
and kitty cats,
the library has got a book.
Come on in,
take a look.
Learn how to cook
or write a poem.
Read it here
or take it home.
What do you want to learn about?
It's free!
It's here!
Check it out!

Poem copyright © 2012 by Sara Holbrook
GREAT Morning! Poems for School Leaders to Read Aloud
by Sylvia Vardell & Janet Wong (Pomelo Books)

DID YOU KNOW?

Did you know that there are many superstitions about how to pass a test? These include:

- Wearing your socks and underwear inside out and your shirt or blouse backward.
- Bringing a lucky rock or some other charm you depend on.
- Using the same pen or pencil you used the last time you passed a test or a new one that has never made a mistake.

Those are just superstitions and won't really help at all. What does help? Doing your best and focusing on success, just like this poem reminds us.

FOLLOW UP

So when it's testing time, remember to "bounce those blues away" and do your best to shine, score, and soar!

CONNECT

For a completely different and nonsensical poem about testing, link with "The World's Most Intelligent Chicken" by Jack Prelutsky (page 118).

Topic 28: Assessment

POETRY PLUS
Also share this poem every time there are big testing dates.

TESTING BLUES
by Xelena González

Bounce those blues
away, away
like that ball you
dribbled & lost
shot & missed
over & over
catching air
before you heard
the sweet *swoosh*
of success.

But if those testing blues
come back,
stand up!
Remember . . .
You *will* shine
You *will* score
You *will* soar!
(You've done it all before.)

DID YOU KNOW?

Approximately 97% of regular readers are currently reading a book for fun or have just finished one. Research has shown that children who are motivated and spend more time reading do better in school. Let's be part of that big number and stop and read every day, just like this poem invites us to do.

FOLLOW UP

Grabbing a spot to read, to look at pictures, to learn new words, and to discover places is such a treat. As Dr. Seuss wrote, "The more that you read, the more things you will know. The more that you learn, the more places you'll go."

CONNECT

Link with a poem that shows everyone in the family reading in some way: "At Our House" by Virginia Euwer Wolff (page 128).

POETRY PLUS

Also share this poem on D.E.A.R. Day (Drop Everything And Read) on April 12.

STOP! LET'S READ

by Kristy Dempsey

Wherever you are,
it's time to stop!
Grab a book
and find a spot.
Look at pictures,
see new faces,
word by word,
discover places.
You say: *Read!*
and I'll join in.
Ready, set,
just begin . . .
Let's start slow
and pick up speed.
Hey, everyone!
It's time to read!

Poem copyright © 2015 by Kristy Dempsey
GREAT Morning! Poems for School Leaders to Read Aloud
by Sylvia Vardell & Janet Wong (Pomelo Books)

DID YOU KNOW?

Do you want to be a philanthropist? That is someone who wants to help other people and support good causes. You don't have to be a grown-up to be a philanthropist. For example, Robbie and Brittany Bergquist, ages 12 and 13, started "Cell Phones for Soldiers" and collected used cell phones and prepaid phone cards so soldiers far away could talk to their families. They raised more than $8 million and sent over 181 million minutes of talk time overseas. This poem shows us another way to help—through participating in a walkathon.

FOLLOW UP

Think about how you can spread hope with every step and support friends in need, too.

CONNECT

For another poem encouraging students to get involved in fundraising and supporting the school, link with "School Bake Sale" by Elaine Magliaro (page 115).

Topic 30: Fundraising

POETRY PLUS

Also share this poem every time there are fundraising or volunteering opportunities.

WALKING FOR A CAUSE

by Catherine Flynn

Hey, kids! Have you heard?
We are walking for a cause.
Ask your parents, neighbors, too,
if they would like to share.
Dollars, quarters, nickels, dimes,
every penny shows we care.

We're spreading hope with every step,
supporting friends in need.
So lace your sneakers, tie them tight.
Come and help our walk succeed!

DID YOU KNOW?

When it comes to building willpower, we all struggle with being strong enough to make tough decisions. Sometimes we have to wait for what we want or say no to things that are tempting or say yes to things we know we should do. Making hard choices, and sticking with them even when the going gets tough, requires willpower. Here's a poem about a challenge that many of us face.

FOLLOW UP

The next time you have to get a shot or injection, try to remember that it will help you win the battle—if you brave the needle!

CONNECT

For another poem about facing challenges, link with "My Experiment" by Julie Larios (page 111).

POETRY PLUS
Also share this poem during World Immunization Week in April.

A SHOT OF COURAGE

by Bob Raczka

Yes, the needle
in your arm will
sting a little,

but your blood will
beat the measles
in a battle,

and the mumps will
run like weasels
from your B cells,

and the flu will
lose a duel
with your T cells.

So if you will
brave the needle,
here's the deal:

You won't be ill.

Poem copyright © 2018 by Bob Raczka
from *GREAT Morning! Poems for School Leaders to Read Aloud*
by Sylvia Vardell & Janet Wong (Pomelo Books)

DID YOU KNOW?

Did you know there are 1,440 minutes in a day? You usually spend 360 minutes here at school in one day, and 64,800 minutes here in one school year! Here's a poem about this minute—this very minute right now.

FOLLOW UP

Take a minute to think about where you are right now. Think about your classroom, your friends, your books; what's right in front of you and all around you. This minute will never come again. Stop and savor it.

CONNECT

For another look at more ways to pause and ponder the moment, link with "A Quiet Day" by Amy Ludwig VanDerwater (page 125).

Topic 32: Mindfulness

POETRY PLUS

Also share this poem on Mindfulness Day on Sept. 12 or any day to encourage calm.

THE HOUSE OF THIS MINUTE

by Kate Coombs

I live in the house of this minute,
where all around me is real.
With freckles and giggles and wiggles,
with sun and rain to feel.

Come live with me in this minute!
We can race and shout and play—
for every day is this minute,
and this minute is every day.

DID YOU KNOW?

Did you know that 80% of Americans have at least one brother or sister? This sibling relationship is the longest relationship most people will have in their whole lives. We might not always get along with our siblings, but they're an important part of our families. This next poem shows one example of the pros and cons of having a sibling.

FOLLOW UP

Sharing with our brothers and sisters is a good thing to do EXCEPT when it comes to things like head lice, bad colds, and sickness in general. Then we try to keep our distance and wash our hands with soap a lot. But with head lice, even washing a lot sometimes doesn't help!

CONNECT

For another poem about an experience with lice, link with "Head Lice Q&A" by April Halprin Wayland (page 126).

POETRY PLUS

Also share this poem on National Child Health Day on the first Monday in October.

GIVING

by Jane Yolen

I have a little brother
Who loves to give me things,
Like small stones from our driveway
And plastic magic rings.

He gives me all his brussels sprouts,
And pennies that he finds.
He loves to hand me ladybugs
And curling orange rinds.

He gives me dandelions,
And little cubes of ice.
And yesterday he brought from school
An itchy head of lice.

Oh, no,
Thanks, Bro.

DID YOU KNOW?

The first smartphone was sold in 1994, weighed more than a pound, was named "Simon," and had a battery that lasted one hour. It was big and clunky and could send an email, but it couldn't browse the internet. Now our cell phones can do so much for us, like allow us to play games, click apps, send texts, take photographs, get directions, buy things, and talk to friends. But are they BETTER than having a friend? This next poem asks that question.

FOLLOW UP

When you feel alone—or need a kind ear, a silly laugh, or a happy smile—remember to turn to a friend and not a phone for the best connection of all.

CONNECT

*Link this poem with a poem about using technology to hear **and see** a loved one far away: "Skype" by Janet Wong (page 133).*

Topic 34: Reaching Out

POETRY PLUS

Share this poem any day to encourage students to reach out to each other.

A PHONE IS NOT A FRIEND

by Carole Boston Weatherford

You don't know you need a friend
Until you're all alone
And realize that a friend is not
The latest mobile phone.
No matter the gigabytes,
That phone can't lend an ear.
An app cannot console you
When you shed a tear.
No matter the emojis,
No phone can ever replace
The ring of shared laughter
And the smile on a friendly face.

DID YOU KNOW?

Park Forest Elementary School in Pennsylvania won a Green Ribbon Schools Award from the U.S. Department of Education for setting an amazing example for their recycling and repurposing. They use the catchphrase "Are you sure?" to help students stop and think which "trash" can be sorted and recycled. In one year, they saved 26 cases of paper towels by teaching everyone to "shake and fold" and use only one paper towel after hand washing. And THEN they composted all their used paper towels, too! Here's a poem to remind us about recycling.

FOLLOW UP

Think about the things you're about to throw away today and stop and ask yourself, "Are you sure?" See if those items can be recycled or even reused and made into something else.

CONNECT

For another poem about how we can show we care for our environment when we recycle, link with "Clean Up" by Janet Wong (page 129).

Topic 35: Clean Up

POETRY PLUS
Also share this poem for Earth Day on April 22 or any day to encourage recycling.

RECYCLING

by Susan Blackaby

Collect the daily scraps and clippings,
gather up the bits and snippings:
Paper, plastic, glass, and tin—
all of these go in the bin.
Once it's sorted and inspected,
so-called waste is redirected.
Think of all the things that you
can make from useful stuff you threw
away!

DID YOU KNOW?

The popsicle was discovered by accident by an 11-year-old boy named Frank Epperson in 1905. He left a cup of powdered drink mix with a stirring stick outside overnight in San Francisco and it froze. Years later in 1923, he patented the "frozen ice on a stick" and named them "Eppsicles," but his kids started calling them "popsicles" and the name has stuck ever since. Two billion popsicles are now sold every year! Here's a field day poem that ends with a popsicle treat.

FOLLOW UP

Have you ever tried running with an egg, spinning a hula hoop, or skipping, slipping, and sliding? They may be old-fashioned activities, but they can be lots of fun. Give them a try and then have a popsicle, too!

CONNECT

When it's time to end the school year, link with "CELEBRATE!" by Joan Bransfield Graham (page 106).

POETRY PLUS
Also share this poem for National Physical Education & Sport Week in May.

FIELD DAY FUN

by Elizabeth Steinglass

Run with an egg!
Hop on one leg!
Keep a hula hoop spinning.

Pull on a rope!
Don't give up hope!
Cheer no matter who's winning.

Skip, slip, and slide!
Belly-flop glide!
Soar with super-kid style.

Play till you plop.
Slurp an ice pop.
Go home with a sticky sweet smile.

DID YOU KNOW?

Did you know that there are nearly a billion microphones manufactured every year? This poem begins with a line about the microphone and ends with a surprise. Listen for the surprise and participate along with me!

FOLLOW UP

Can you imagine our school with no students? Soon the school year will end and our building will be closed, cleaned up, and prepared for next year. We look forward to your return and filling the halls with students again!

CONNECT

Link with "Summer Reading" by Janet Wong (page 134) for another poem for the end of the school year. If time allows, read this linked poem to encourage students to read all summer long—to prevent "Summer Slide" and losing gains made during the school year.

POETRY PLUS

Also share this poem on teacher in-service days when students are absent.

IS ANYBODY OUT THERE?

by Brod Bagert

I'm talking to my microphone
with lots of stuff to say,
but what if not a single kid
showed up for school today?

A school without the children. Oh!
It chills me to the bone.
Every table, every desk,
every teacher all alone.

Is anybody out there?
It fills my heart with doubt.
If anybody's out there I
would love to hear you shout!

POETRY TEACHES US THE POWER OF A FEW WORDS.

RALPH WALDO EMERSON

POEM LINKS

This *Poem Links* section includes **more poems linked with each of the previous featured poems.** Each poem pair shares a common theme or subject identified in the "CONNECT" portion of each activity.

4
If time allows, read aloud the **"CONNECT"** linked poem.

CONNECT

You can read the linked poems along with the featured poems in one setting at the same time or one after the other in the same week to provide reinforcement. Teachers and librarians can share the linked poem in classrooms or in the library and even teach a mini-lesson on a related language skill through the poem, pointing out the **Hidden Language Skills** highlighted on pages 139-143.

In addition, you can save or repeat these linked poems for special occasions or relevant celebrations, such as National Library Week (for sharing "Thankful" by Traci Sorell on page 121, for example). Plus, the Subject Index on pages 162-163 allows you to search ALL the poems for a "just right" poem for any day or occasion.

POETRY LINK
This poem is linked with "How to Make a Friend" by Jane Heitman Healy, p. 27.

BILINGUAL

by Alma Flor Ada

Because I speak Spanish
I can listen to my grandmother's stories
and say *familia, madre, amor.*
Because I speak English
I can learn from my teacher
and say **I love school**.
Because I am bilingual
I can read *libros* and **books**,
I have *amigos* and **friends**,
enjoy *canciones* and **songs**,
juegos and **games**
and have twice as much fun.
And someday,
because I speak two languages,
I will be able to do twice as much
to help twice as many people
and be twice as good in what I do.

POETRY BONUS
Hear this poem read aloud in Chinese at PomeloBooks.com.

Poem copyright © 2015 by Alma Flor Ada
GREAT Morning! Poems for School Leaders to Read Aloud
by Sylvia Vardell & Janet Wong (Pomelo Books)

POETRY LINK
This poem is linked with "How to Make a Friend" by Jane Heitman Healy, p. 27.

BILINGÜE

por Alma Flor Ada

Porque hablo español
puedo escuchar los cuentos de abuelita
y decir **familia, madre, amor.**
Porque hablo inglés
puedo aprender de mi maestra
y decir *I love school.*
Porque soy bilingüe
puedo leer **libros** y *books*,
tengo **amigos** y *friends*,
disfruto **canciones** y *songs*,
juegos y *games*
¡y me divierto el doble!
Y algún día,
porque hablo dos idiomas,
podré hacer doble esfuerzo
para ayudar al doble de personas
y lo haré todo el doble de bien.

POETRY BONUS
Listen to this poem read aloud in Spanish and English at Soundcloud.com.

POETRY LINK
This poem is linked with "#1 and A++" by Janet Wong, p. 47.

SINCERELY

by Robyn Hood Black

Dear Friend,

I see the thoughtful things you do.
Your words are always cheerful, too.

I noticed!
And I'm thanking you.

Sincerely,
Me

POETRY BONUS
Look for a digital "postcard" of this poem at Pinterest.com/ PomeloBooks.

POETRY LINK
This poem is linked with "Gym Teachers" by Darren Sardelli, p. 57.

LET'S GO

by Merry Bradshaw

Stretch High
Stretch Wide
Jump Forward
Jump Back

Lean Left
Lean Right
Hop Once
Hop Twice

Reach Up
Reach Down
Twist Small
Twist Tall

Shake Fast
Shake Slow
Touch Nose
Touch Toes

Stand Up
Let's Go!

Poem copyright © 2015 by Merry Bradshaw
GREAT Morning! Poems for School Leaders to Read Aloud
by Sylvia Vardell & Janet Wong (Pomelo Books)

IN THE LIFE
OF A SUBSTITUTE

by Lydia Breiseth

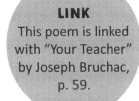

POETRY LINK
This poem is linked with "Your Teacher" by Joseph Bruchac, p. 59.

Before the sun rises,
I hear the phone ring.
In the life of a substitute,
That means just one thing!

A teacher is absent.
I must save the day!
To help teach the lessons
As kids learn and play.

What will the class be?
Will I teach kids to read?
Will we learn to compare
A plant spore and a seed?

Or perhaps do some history
Or music or art
Or writing a poem!
Where should we start?

One thing is certain
That I know to be true—
Each day as a substitute,
I learn something new!

POETRY BONUS
This is an example of a "question poem." For more info, see p. 142.

POETRY LINK

This poem is linked with "When You Arrived: A Birthday Poem" by Liz Garton Scanlon, p. 53.

WINTER COUNTING
by Joseph Bruchac

How many winters
do you have?
That's how we ask
someone their age.

The snow that fell,
then melted away,
reminds us that
we still are here.

It's easy to count
your age by years.
We think winter counting
is a better way.

It makes us grateful
for the spring
when every bird
and every flower
welcomes us to
a whole new time.

Then sunshine is
in every heart
and we smile
as we ask each other
how many winters
do you have now?

POETRY BONUS

Zeller's Algorithm tells what day of the week you were born on. See Interactive-Maths.com/Zellers-Algorithm.

WHAT IS SCIENCE?
by Cynthia Cotten

Science is
knowledge
and
a process

Science is
how and why (or why not)
experimentation and observation
expected results and accidental discoveries

Science is
questioning
exploring
understanding

Science is
useful
exciting
ongoing
challenging

Science is
the study of
elements, compounds, cells
motion, sound, light
and of
the ocean,
the earth,
the sky,
and all that they contain

With all that science *is*
perhaps the question should be
"What *isn't* science?"

POETRY LINK
This poem is linked with "Science Fair" by Eric Ode, p. 69.

POETRY BONUS
This poem is also featured in NSTA's *Science and Children* journal in the monthly "Poetry of Science" column.

POETRY LINK

This poem is linked with "What Does a Reading Specialist Do?" by Linda Kulp Trout, p. 61.

SECRET WORLDS

by Margarita Engle

Please don't worry or fret today.
Just enjoy one page at a time.
Read a story, or poems that rhyme.
Write if you have something to say.

Each book is like a passageway
to secret worlds where you can play.

Reading will take you far away
to mountain peaks that you can climb
or dark swamps filled with thick green slime.
(Read backwards if you lose your way!)

Note: This poetic form is a Cuban décima mirror (see Hidden Language Skills, page 143).

POETRY BONUS

Learn more about the Young People's Poet Laureate at PoetryFoundation.org.

POETRY LINK
This poem is linked with "Oh, Those Forms!" by Janet Clare Fagal, p. 21.

WHO AM I?

by Margarita Engle

Each time I have to fill out a form
that demands my ethnic origin, I try
to do the math. Half this, half that,
with grandparents who were probably
half something else, or maybe
a quarter,
or an eighth.

Why do forms always ask
what I am, instead of asking
who?

POETRY BONUS
Look for a digital "postcard" of this poem at Pinterest.com/ PomeloBooks.

POETRY LINK
This poem is linked with "Field Day Fun" by Elizabeth Steinglass, p. 91.

CELEBRATE!

by Joan Bransfield Graham

I've seen you working
all year long.
I like your spirit—
focused, strong.

Exploring, learning,
making friends—
another year together
ends.

So now this principal
proclaims . . .
it's time for food, treats,
fun, and games.

You're one year smarter,
looking GREAT.
Hooray—it's time to
CELEBRATE!

POETRY BONUS
This poem demonstrates the power of alignment. For more info, see p. 139.

POETRY LINK
This poem is linked with "Photo Op" by Linda Sue Park, p. 29.

SELFIE

by Lorie Ann Grover

Smile
Laugh
Click
Pic
See?
Me!

POETRY BONUS
Look for a digital "postcard" of this poem at Pinterest.com/ PomeloBooks.

POETRY LINK
This poem is linked with "Report Cards" by Janet Wong, p. 39.

COMPLIMENT CHAIN

by Mary Lee Hahn

Your two small words
Good job!
filled me up.
I sat straighter in my chair.
I *had* worked hard.
And you noticed.

My friend
is bent over his paper.
His pencil moves slowly, carefully.
I say two small words,
Good job!
And watch him sit up straight.

POETRY BONUS
Look for a digital "postcard" of this poem at Pinterest.com/ PomeloBooks.

POETRY LINK
This poem is linked with "Make a Joyful Noise" by B.J. Lee, p. 65.

MY KINDERGARTEN CHOIR

by Avis Harley

My aunt and uncle, mom and dad,
have come to hear my choir.
I'm standing on the bench behind
the kids who sing up higher.

It's hard to see beyond the lights
what row my folks are in,
but if I wave they'll find me quick
before the songs begin.

POETRY BONUS
This poem demonstrates the use of contractions. For more info, go to p. 141.

POETRY LINK

This poem is linked with "To Our Front Office Staff" by Kay Winters, p. 41.

OUR CUSTODIAN

by Ann Ingalls

Our custodian
Welcomes everyone each day.
Carries packages.
Holds the door for others.
Makes coffee for the teachers.

Fills the bird feeders.
Finds class pets when they go missing.
Waves goodbye at the end of the day.
Oh, and I forgot to say,
Cleans the building, too.

POETRY BONUS

This is a great example of a list poem. For more info, see p. 140.

Poem copyright © 2018 by Ann Ingalls
from *GREAT Morning! Poems for School Leaders to Read Aloud*
by Sylvia Vardell & Janet Wong (Pomelo Books)

POETRY LINK

This poem is linked with "A Shot of Courage" by Bob Raczka, p. 81.

MY EXPERIMENT

by Julie Larios

I tried each possibility,
I tried it all, I tried my best,
I tried to think, I tried to see,
I tried things out, I didn't rest,
I thought I had it, I thought I knew,
I thought what I had was good and true,
but the bottom caved in, the top spilled out,
I couldn't figure the darn thing out,
it all collapsed, it all fell down,
the smile I smiled became a frown.
I didn't succeed, so tomorrow is when
I have to try and try again.
That's good advice, that's right, I guess—
but meanwhile (*sigh) what an awful mess.

POETRY BONUS

Check out poet Julie Larios's blog, *The Drift Record*. More info at p. 155.

POETRY LINK

This poem is linked with "All Kinds of Kids" by Elizabeth Steinglass, p. 43.

FRIENDS

by Renée M. LaTulippe

Annie
has a chair on wheels.
She's fast
and she can spin!
We race each other
after school.
Sometimes she lets me win.

Robert
doesn't talk like me,
but draws
a whole lot better.
He points out pictures
in our books,
and I point out each letter.

Lucy
moves her hands to speak,
her fingers
forming shapes.
We are silent
superheroes
in our masks and capes.

My friends and I
are different,
but not in every way.
All of us love having fun—
we read
and draw
and play!

POETRY BONUS

Share this poem again on Dec. 3, the International Day of Persons with Disabilities.

Poem copyright © 2015 by Renée M. LaTulippe
from *GREAT Morning! Poems for School Leaders to Read Aloud*
by Sylvia Vardell & Janet Wong (Pomelo Books)

POETRY LINK
This poem is linked with "Art Class" by Carol Varsalona, p. 63.

VIRTUAL ADVENTURE

by Renée M. LaTulippe

Yesterday I scaled some peaks.
Looky here: wind-chapped cheeks!

Right after lunch, I rode a gnu,
caught cuckoo birds in Katmandu.

Snowboard? Check. Windsurf, scuba.
After dinner? Played a tuba.

Safari in the Serengeti,
tango with a sweaty yeti.

I can do most anything—

from biking in downtown Beijing
to wrestling deep-sea squid-eos—

with my green screen videos.

POETRY BONUS
Go to MakerSpace ForEducation.com/ green-screen-technology to learn more about green screens for kids.

Poem copyright © 2014 by Renée M. LaTulippe
GREAT Morning! Poems for School Leaders to Read Aloud
by Sylvia Vardell & Janet Wong (Pomelo Books)

POETRY LINK

This poem is linked with "We'll Keep Safe" by Janet Wong, p. 23.

BEEP, BEEP, BEEP!

by Suzy Levinson

Make a fire safety plan!
First thing you should know . . .
smoke alarms say *beep, beep, beep*!
That means you should go!

Pick a nearby meeting place,
a mailbox or a tree.
Just as quick as *beep, beep, beep*,
join your family.

Why not practice more than one
method of escape?
Then if there's a *beep, beep, beep*,
you're in tip-top shape!

POETRY BONUS

Go to USFA.FEMA.gov/prevention for more fire safety tips.

Poem copyright © 2015 by Suzy Levinson
from *GREAT Morning! Poems for School Leaders to Read Aloud*
by Sylvia Vardell & Janet Wong (Pomelo Books)

POETRY LINK

This poem is linked with "Walking for a Cause" by Catherine Flynn, p. 79.

SCHOOL BAKE SALE

by Elaine Magliaro

We're having a bake sale tomorrow at three.
We're raising money for our school's library.
We'll have goodies to sell—goodies galore—
Better than baked goods you buy in a store:
Cranberry muffins and cinnamon rolls,
Pretzels, turnovers, scones, donut holes,
Sweet Danish pastries slathered with jam,
Calzones stuffed with cheddar and ham,
Frosted brownies—fudgy and gooey—
Tart lemon squares—tangy and chewy—
Flaky fruit pies bursting with berries,
Peaches, apples, rhubarb, and cherries,
Coconut cream cakes, cookies, and more!
We'll have goodies to sell—goodies galore.
Come to our bake sale tomorrow at three!
Help us raise money for our school's library.

POETRY BONUS

Did you spot the alliteration in this poem? See p. 139 for more info.

Poem copyright © 2018 by Elaine Magliaro
from GREAT Morning! Poems for School Leaders to Read Aloud
by Sylvia Vardell & Janet Wong (Pomelo Books)

POETRY LINK
This poem is linked with "School Nurse" by Elizabeth Steinglass, p. 33.

I WONDER WHO

by Eric Ode

I wonder who takes care of her
whenever she's not well.
Who bandages her elbows
if she stumbled or she fell?

And if she has a stomachache,
or if her nose is runny,
who brings her favorite teddy bear
and makes her tea with honey?

Who's there to take her temperature?
Who puts her down to bed?
Who gives her bowls of chicken soup
and kisses on her head?

It's never fun to be the one
who's hurt or sick or worse.
But now and then I wonder,
who is there to help the nurse?

POETRY BONUS
Eric Ode writes songs as well as poems. See EricOde.com/ Blog for more info.

POETRY LINK
This poem is linked with "Recess" by Avis Harley, p. 55.

TIME FOR SCHOOL

by Ann Whitford Paul

It's time for school—
sitting-at-your-desk time,
talking-only-when-called-on time,
hard-to-keep-from-fidgeting time,
until
    the bell rings.
        Out you go!
Race! Chase! Slide! Swing!
Whoop! Holler! Shout! Scream!
Be a teapot! Spout out steam!
It's recess time!

POETRY BONUS
Use this poem to discuss punctuation (e.g., hyphens) with children.
See p. 141.

Poem copyright © 2018 by Ann Whitford Paul
from *GREAT Morning! Poems for School Leaders to Read Aloud*
by Sylvia Vardell & Janet Wong (Pomelo Books)

POETRY LINK

This poem is linked with "Testing Blues" by Xelena González, p. 75.

THE WORLD'S MOST INTELLIGENT CHICKEN

by Jack Prelutsky

The world's most intelligent chicken,
As well as the world's wisest duck,
Were challenged to take an IQ test—
They agreed with a quack and a cluck.
For fowl that were rated so highly,
Their knowledge turned out to be small.
In fact, it was quickly apparent
They knew nearly nothing at all.

They thought that an ibis had petals,
They thought that an iris had wings.
They thought that potatoes grew feathers,
They thought that a cantaloupe sings.
They thought that a floor needed windows,
That apples grew under the sea,
That clocks always ran counterclockwise,
And eight minus seven was three.

They struggled with every last question
On science, math, music, and art.
You'd never suspect, from their answers,
That they were supposed to be smart.
They filled in the blanks incorrectly,
Their two little brains remained stuck . . .
A chicken is only a chicken,
A duck is no more than a duck.

POETRY BONUS

This is a fun example of a narrative poem. For more info, see p. 140.

Poem copyright © 2012 by Jack Prelutsky
from *GREAT Morning! Poems for School Leaders to Read Aloud*
by Sylvia Vardell & Janet Wong (Pomelo Books)

POETRY LINK
This poem is linked with "On Your Way to School" by Laura Purdie Salas, p. 45.

BICYCLE DREAMS

by Michael Salinger

my wheels are spinning
pedals are turning
hands on the handlebars
as I roll along
training wheels gone
a bike riding superstar
my thumb rings the bell
as I speed down the block
wind whooshes through my hair
I love riding my bike
'cause it makes me feel
like I can go anywhere

Note: Unlike driving a car or riding a bus, pedaling a bicycle makes the rider both the engine and the driver. It's the closest we can come to self-powered flying!

POETRY BONUS
Share this poem again in May for National Bike Month.

POETRY LINK

This poem is linked with "Today's the Day" by Greg Pincus, p. 71.

NO KIDDING

by Michelle Schaub

Do riddles make you giggle?
Do knock knocks make you grin?
Do silly words and stories
give tickles to your skin?
If you tend to chuckle
when your funny bone is poked,
don't miss this day for kidding—
go share your favorite joke!

POETRY BONUS

Look for a digital "postcard" of this poem at Pinterest.com/ PomeloBooks.

Poem copyright © 2015 by Michelle Schaub
from *GREAT Morning! Poems for School Leaders to Read Aloud*
by Sylvia Vardell & Janet Wong (Pomelo Books)

POETRY LINK
This poem is linked with "The Library" by Sara Holbrook, p. 73.

THANKFUL

by Traci Sorell

I am thankful for
. . . thousands of stories to read.
. . . fun, fact-finding computers.
. . . quiet space to study and dream.

I am thankful for
. . . my school library.

POETRY BONUS
Share this poem again in April to celebrate School Library Month.

POETRY LINK
This poem is linked with "Scary Territory" by Janet Wong, p. 49.

POEM FOR A BULLY

by Eileen Spinelli

Somewhere deep inside you
there's a softer, kinder place.
I know this will surprise you—
but I've seen it in your face.
Your eyes are often sad, although
you wear a surly grin.
Sometimes when you stand all alone
your "mean" seems worn and thin.
I wish that you would take a step—
a small but brave one, too—
and look inside yourself to find
the good I see in you.

POETRY BONUS
Look for a digital "postcard" of this poem at Pinterest.com/PomeloBooks.

THINGS NOT TO DO

by Eileen Spinelli

POETRY LINK
This poem is linked with "Time for Lunch" by Caroline Starr Rose, p. 25.

Don't pick your nose.
Don't push in line.
Don't grab for things.
Don't stomp. Don't whine.

Don't slurp your soup.
Don't burp. And please
don't sneeze into
your sister's peas.

Don't say mean things.
Don't lie. Don't litter.
Don't hide to scare
the babysitter.

Don't grumble when
you're doing chores.
Don't mumble words.
And don't slam doors.

And while you're at it
don't forget—
life's nicer with
good etiquette.

POETRY BONUS
Share this poem again in early May for National Etiquette Week.

POETRY LINK

This poem is linked with "Cat Coder" by Buffy Silverman, p. 67.

TECH TODAY

by Holly Thompson

when it's time to project
it's time to connect
projectors and cables
computers, remotes

we've got this, no sweat!
we plug this into that
we hook that up to this
looks correct! we're all set!

except . . .

time to start over
let's try it once more
start over, disconnect
okay, now we're all set
we've checked and rechecked

hold your breath,
will it work?
let's reconnect . . . yay!
we can use the projector today

POETRY BONUS

This poem uses only lower case letters. For more about the use of capitalization in poetry, see p. 139.

POETRY LINK
This poem is linked with "The House of This Minute" by Kate Coombs, p. 83.

A QUIET DAY

by Amy Ludwig VanDerwater

A quiet day is like a park.
You can be alone.
You can play hide-and-seek inside your brain.
You can remember everything you ever did.
You can dream.
You can draw a picture.
You can be you
sitting in the sunshine
thinking thoughts on your own bench
watching squirrels run around in your head.
You can even bring a book.

POETRY BONUS
This poet models many writing strategies at Sharing OurNotebooks. AmyLV.com.

Poem copyright © 2012 by Amy Ludwig VanDerwater
GREAT Morning! Poems for School Leaders to Read Aloud
by Sylvia Vardell & Janet Wong (Pomelo Books)

POETRY LINK
This poem is linked with "Giving" by Jane Yolen, p. 85.

HEAD LICE Q&A

by April Halprin Wayland

Q:
I itch, I scratch—did I do something bad?
My head feels like a launching pad!

A:
We're head lice, we love heads and hair
come dine with us, it's nice up here
(oh, don't forget to bring the salt)
*and heavens, no—**it's not your fault!***

POETRY BONUS
Check out MedlinePlus.gov for additional info on dealing with head lice.

THE MOST GLAD-TO-SEE DAY OF THE YEAR

by Allan Wolf

POETRY LINK
This poem is linked with "GREAT Morning!" by Janet Wong, p. 19.

My favorite, special, most glad-to-see day,
the day I consider the best.
The day when I really get carried away.
The top day all year! Can you guess?

It isn't my birthday. It isn't Thanksgiving.
And no, it's not Hanukkah, Christmas, and all.
It's not Halloween that makes life so worth living.
My day happens Spring, Summer, Winter, and Fall.

It's not a one-timer. My day never ends.
It's the first, second, middle, and last.
It is here, holy cow! It is new. It is now.
It is not in the future or past.

I'll give you the answer: My day is . . . Today!
There's no waiting in line. There is no long delay.
What yesterday was and tomorrow will be,
Today's the most wonderful day for me.

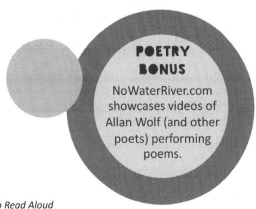

POETRY BONUS
NoWaterRiver.com showcases videos of Allan Wolf (and other poets) performing poems.

POETRY LINK
This poem is linked with "STOP! Let's Read" by Kristy Dempsey, p. 77.

AT OUR HOUSE

by Virginia Euwer Wolff

Dad reads to me while he makes me lunch,
Mom reads to me in bed.
My little brother wants to hear
every word that we have read.

Grandpa's learning how to read,
Grandma hums along.
Books speak right up in our house,
and words turn into song.

POETRY BONUS

Share this poem again on Nov. 1 for National Family Literacy Day.

CLEAN UP

by Janet Wong

When it's time for us
to pitch in
and clean up

It would be simple
just
to dump

Everything
in the regular
trash

But that would be sloppy,
slipshod,
slapdash—

And when we recycle
we're showing
we care

We don't
just toss things
anywhere

We think
while we sort
and clean up neatly—

We do our job well
and we do it
completely!

POETRY LINK
This poem is linked with "Recycling" by Susan Blackaby, p. 89.

POETRY BONUS
This poem models the use of tercets. Find more info on stanzas on p. 143.

POETRY LINK
This poem is linked with "Look for the Helpers" by Michelle Heidenrich Barnes, p. 35.

IF YOU SEE SOMETHING, SAY SOMETHING

by Janet Wong

You've probably heard people say:
"If you see something, say something."

It sounds simple.
It sounds clear—

but sometimes
even when you're standing near

you might not be sure
what you saw. What you heard.

Come talk.
I'll be your sounding board.

Come say what you're feeling.
Come speak your mind.

I'm here to help.
I'll make the time.

POETRY BONUS
Present this poem with caution tape as a prop. See Poetry Suitcase tips at JanetWong.com.

LET'S PLEDGE BETWEEN US

by Janet Wong

POETRY LINK
This poem is linked with "Principal for a Day" by Laura Shovan, p. 37.

Let's pledge between us:
to be kind

and remind ourselves every morning
to be respectful and honest and true,

each person
looking out
for the other,

doing what's right,
acting responsibly
in fairness
for all.

POETRY BONUS

Here the poet uses the Pledge of Allegiance as a model for this poem.

POETRY LINK
This poem is linked with "Food Fest" by Heidi Bee Roemer, p. 31.

LUNCHTIME

by Janet Wong

Lunchtime is
    time for gratitude
    a half hour of
    nourishment.

Lunchtime is
    time to sit with a friend
    for talk-till-the-end
    encouragement.

Nourishment.
Encouragement.
Lunch is meant
to be many things.

I just wish
that once in a while
we could have onion rings!

POETRY BONUS
Notice how the poet uses *italics* for emphasis in this poem. See also: p. 140.

POETRY LINK
This poem is linked with "A Phone Is Not a Friend" by Carole Boston Weatherford, p. 87.

SKYPE

by Janet Wong

Once a month
we Skype with Dad
who's in the army.
I'm so glad
that he can tell
how tall I've grown.
You can't see
on our telephone—
but here
with our computer screen
he knows exactly
what we mean
when Mom says
I'm a big kid now.
His eyes glow
when he says,
"I'm proud."

POETRY BONUS
Go to MilitaryFamily.org for more info about life for military families.

POETRY LINK
This poem is linked with "Is Anybody Out There?" by Brod Bagert p. 93.

SUMMER READING

by Janet Wong

If you're simmering this summer—
suffering in sweat and heat—
an air-conditioned library
is OH-SO-SWEET!

Grab a book and sit a while.
Summer reading is so cool!
Relax. Recharge. Get ready
for The First Day of School!

POETRY BONUS

Get ready for Summer Reading Month (June) with this fun poem.

POETRY LINK
This poem is linked with "New Year Is Here" by Kenn Nesbitt, p. 51.

WHAT WE'RE LEARNING

by Janet Wong

Nelson is learning fractions.
Ella is learning to spell.
Winnie is learning how to paint.

She paints trees really well.
Kim is learning robotics.
Ingrid is learning to code.
Leon is learning three
Languages. We're all in
Skill-building Mode!

POETRY BONUS

This poem is an acrostic. Read more about this poem form on p. 139.

POETRY IS A LOVELY GIFT
WE GIVE TO CHILDREN
THAT APPRECIATES IN VALUE
AND LASTS THROUGHOUT
THEIR LIFETIMES.

MARIA BROUNTAS

MORE POETRY RESOURCES

PRINCIPALS AS PARTNERS

As school leaders, principals can establish the literacy culture of the school. Reading a poem during the morning announcements is one easy way to communicate this powerful priority. Then this simple poem can become part of school-wide literacy lessons that are continued by other members of the literacy team all week long, including teachers, librarians, specialists, and even families and community members.

Here are three possible ways to use this book:
1. Principals or other school leaders can read a poem during morning announcements;
2. Classroom teachers, librarians, or reading specialists can read the linked poems as a follow-up during the same week;
3. Teachers and reading specialists can also introduce the poem's "Hidden Language Skills" or use the *Take 5!* activities for selected poems.

What Are Hidden Language Skills?

Sharing each poem for the pleasure of the words and meaning is the first step. And that can set the stage for inductive skill teaching, too. **We have identified a "hidden" language or poetry skill for EVERY poem in this book** to make it easy to connect these poems with planned skill instruction. In addition, books in *The Poetry Friday Anthology* series take this approach a step further with *Take 5!* activities for hundreds of poems with skill instruction explicitly identified in the context of reading aloud, discussing, and enjoying each poem—all in approximately five minutes.

For the poems in **this** book, you can find many examples for lessons on general language arts skills (such as capitalization and punctuation), as well as specific poetry skills (such as alliteration and simile). While each poem can be helpful for highlighting a variety of language or poetry skills, we recommend choosing just ONE skill focus for any ONE poem, for maximum clarity and to keep the fun in sharing poems, too. EVERY poem here is connected with at least one potential language or poetry skill including:

Acrostic Poem	Letter Poem	Punctuation
Alliteration	List Poem	Question Poem
Alignment	Lyrical Poem	Repetition
Analogy	Metaphor	Rhyme
Capitalization	Narrative Poem	Rhythm
Dialogue	Number Concepts	Simile
Font	Onomatopoeia	Stanzas
Free Verse	Personification	Unusual Forms
Humor	Poem of Address	Vivid Vocabulary

HIDDEN LANGUAGE SKILLS

Here are some of the most commonly taught poetry and language skills linked with all the poems presented throughout this book.

Acrostic Poem: A poem form where the first letters of each line spell a word when read vertically.

> "What We're Learning" (p. 135): the first letters spell NEW SKILLS

Alliteration: Placing words that start with the same letter/sound near each other.

> "School Nurse" (p.33): *slip scrape, get gooey, head hot*
> "Science Fair" (p. 69): *clearly catalogued, vinegar volcanoes*
> "School Bake Sale" (p. 115): *goodies galore, flaky fruit*
> "Thankful" (p. 121): *thankful, thousands, fun, fact-finding*

Alignment: Poets use line breaks (alignment) for various reasons: creating visual interest, giving clues for reading a poem, emphasizing meaning, and more.

> "To Our Front Office Staff: A Celebration" (p. 41): scattered lines
> "On Your Way to School" (p. 45): short lines followed by long lines
> "Recycling" (p. 89): "away" is "thrown" onto a separate line
> "CELEBRATE!" (p. 106): lines of alternating length

Analogy: A device that uses familiar things to connect unfamiliar things.

> "Food Fest" (p. 31): *Chef* is connected with *teacher* (an unlikely pair) by using familiar associations for those words: *restaurant* and *school*

Capitalization: Poets often play with capitalization, sometimes putting selected words in all capital letters to emphasize meaning. They also sometimes use no capital letters at all; when this is done, there is often little or no punctuation as well. Poems can also serve as instructional texts to teach capitalization conventions, such as capitalizing the first letter of a proper noun ("Fridays") or capitalizing all letters of an acronym ("STEM").

> **Proper Nouns and Acronyms**: "Poetry Fridays" (p. 17; days of the week); "At Our House" (p. 128; family names); "Friends" (p. 112; first names)

> **All Capitals**: "GREAT Morning!" (p. 19); "Photo Op" (p. 29; *CHEESE, FLEAS*)

> **Mainly/All Lowercase**: "Bicycle Dreams" (p. 119); "Tech Today" (p. 124)

> **NOTE:** An interesting thing to point out to older students is that sometimes poets capitalize the first letter in each line, and other times poets capitalize only the first word in a clearly marked sentence: "Look for the Helpers" (p. 35); "How to Make a Friend" (p. 27); "Skype" (p. 133)

Dialogue: Sometimes poets use phrases, lines, and stanzas within quotation marks as if someone were speaking.

> "Photo Op" (p. 29)
> "If You See Something, Say Something" (p. 130)
> "Skype" (p. 133)

Font: Font styles and elements, such as putting text in italics, bold, or using underlining, can emphasize meaning.

> **Italics:** Italic type is a cursive font that writers often use to emphasize meaning or signal changes in speaker or language.
>> "How to Make a Friend" (p. 27): words of greeting are italicized
>> "Compliment Chain" (p. 108): italics are used to denote speech (*Good job!*) and also to emphasize meaning (I *had* worked hard)
>> "Who Am I?" (p. 105): key words are italicized (*what, who*)
>> "Lunchtime" (p. 132): key words are italicized (*nourishment, encouragement*)

> **Bold:** Bold type can be used for emphasis, often as a substitute for underlining, but sometimes with underlining, too.
>> "Head Lice Q&A" (p. 126): the "A" (Answer) voice is italicized, with the most important point also in bold
>> "Bilingual" (p. 97) and "Bilingüe" (p. 98): the key words are italicized and in bold

Free Verse: A poem that does not seem to follow the rules of a poetic form.
"When You Arrived: A Birthday Poem" (p. 53); "A Quiet Day" (p. 125)

Humor: Many poets use humor in their poems.
"Science Fair" (p. 69); "Today's the Day" (p. 71); "Giving" (p. 85); "The World's Most Intelligent Chicken" (p. 118)

Letter Poem: A poem in the form of a letter (also called an "epistolary poem"). You can use this type of poem to introduce the parts of a letter (greeting/salutation, body, closing, etc.)
"Sincerely" (p. 99)

List Poem: A poem that lists similar words, often examples strung together to illustrate a concept or support an idea.
"Oh, Those Forms" (p. 21); "Recess" (p. 55); "The Library" (p. 73); "Our Custodian" (p. 110); "School Bake Sale" (p. 115)

Lyrical Poem: A first-person reflection on the poet's feelings.
"Bilingual" (p. 97); "Who Am I?" (p. 105)

Metaphor: A device where one thing is compared to another, often in unspoken terms.
"When You Arrived: A Birthday Poem" (p. 53): *you were given a gift— your own day* (your birth date is a kind of present)
"The House of This Minute" (p. 83): *I live in the house of this minute* (I am thinking in terms of the present)

Narrative Poem: A poem that tells a story.

Number Concepts:

 Words and Symbols: Teach number/sequence words and symbols.
 "Who Am I?" (p. 105): *half, quarter, eighth*
 "#1 and A++" (p. 47): # and +
 "The Most Glad-to-See Day of the Year" (p. 127): *first, second, middle, and last*

 Sequencing: Sometimes poets put words and lines in a specific order or sequence.
 "Poetry Fridays" (p. 17)
 "Selfie" (p. 107)

Onomatopoeia: Words that sound like what they mean.
 "Make a Joyful Noise" (p. 65): *Rum-tum-tum; Bang; Clack; toot*
 "Testing Blues" (p. 75): *swoosh*
 "Beep, Beep, Beep!" (p. 114): *beep, beep, beep*

Personification: Words and phrases that give inanimate objects human characteristics.
 "Cat Coder" (p. 67): *cats can dance; cats sashay*
 "A Shot of Courage" (p. 81): *blood will beat the measles; mumps will run; flu will lose a duel*
 "A Phone Is Not a Friend" (p. 87): *phone can't lend an ear; an app cannot console you*

Poem of Address: A poem where the word "you" is used to show that someone is being spoken to.
 "Walking for a Cause" (p. 79); "Poem for a Bully" (p. 122); "Your Teacher" (p. 59)

Punctuation: Poems use the whole spectrum of punctuation marks. Here are some particularly interesting examples.

 Apostrophe (possessive): "Science Fair" (p. 69)

 Contractions: "My Kindergarten Choir" (page 109); "I Wonder Who" (p. 116); "We'll Keep Safe" (p. 23)

 Ellipses: "Tech Today" (p. 124); "Thankful" (p. 121)

 Exclamation Mark: "GREAT Morning!" (p. 19); "All Kinds of Kids" (p. 43); "New Year Is Here" (p. 51); "STOP! Let's Read" (p. 77)

 Hyphens: "Time for School" (p. 117); "Summer Reading" (p. 134); "The Most Glad-to-See Day of the Year" (p. 127)

 Question Marks: "What Is Science?" (p. 103); "No Kidding" (p. 120)

 NOTE: Poets sometimes use little/no punctuation: "Art Class" (p. 63); "Let's Go" (p. 100)

Question Poem: Poems that raise or answer questions.
> "In the Life of a Substitute" (p. 101); "Winter Counting" (p. 102); "What Is Science?" (p. 103)

Repetition: Repeated words, phrases, or lines can often enhance meaning and add emphasis.
> "Time for Lunch" (p. 25): line 1 (used 3 times) and line 2 (used twice)
> "Scary Territory" (p. 49): *saying sorry* (used 4 times)
> "New Year Is Here" (p. 51): *New* (used 13 times)
> "Things Not to Do" (p. 123): *Don't* (used 15 times)
> "My Experiment" (p. 111): *I tried* (used 6 times)

> **NOTE:** Sometimes a line is repeated with just one or two words changed for emphasis, such as in "Oh, Those Forms!" (p. 21): *School forms are quite important* (Stanza 1); *ALL forms are quite important* (Stanza 3).

Rhyme: There are many types of rhymes. The traditional way to use rhyme is to place exact rhymes (or perfect rhymes) at the ends of lines, but this need not be the case. Additional concepts to introduce:

> **Near Rhyme** (off/slant/sight rhyme): words that almost rhyme. "Scary Territory" (p. 49): *sorry, worry*

> **Internal Rhyme:** rhymes that occur within a line. "Virtual Adventure" (p. 113): *sweaty yeti; green screen*

> **Rhymes with Different Spellings:** "Things Not to Do" (p. 123): *please, peas; chores, doors*

> **NOTE:** You can also discuss stanzas when you talk about rhyme, since rhyming poems are usually arranged in stanzas.

Rhythm: We can say that a text has a strong rhythm when it has a regular meter or pattern of beats, especially when those beats (or stresses or feet) can be counted. The most common rhythmic patterns are:
> **iamb:** ⌣ / (ex: about)
> **trochee:** / ⌣ (ex: happy; soccer)
> **anapest:** ⌣ ⌣ / (ex: understand; of the game)
> **dactyl:** / ⌣ ⌣ (ex: yesterday)

Here are some poems with a strong rhythm:
> "Oh, Those Forms!" (p. 21); "Recess" (p. 55); "Gym Teachers" (p. 57); "The World's Most Intelligent Chicken" (p. 118)

Simile: A device where "like" or "as" is used to compare one thing to another.

Here are some examples of poems using similes:

"Report Cards" (p. 39): *like a photo*
"Gym Teachers" (p. 57): *noble as knights*
"What Does a Reading Specialist Do?" (p. 61): *Like a detective*
"Secret Worlds" (p. 104): *like a passageway*
"A Quiet Day" (p. 125): *like a park*
"Head Lice Q&A" (p. 126): *like a launching pad*

Stanzas: Lines grouped together and set off by spaces ("stanza breaks"). Stanzas don't need to rhyme, but we usually see rhyming poems arranged in stanzas.

Couplets (stanzas of two lines each; or two successive lines that rhyme): "Food Fest" (p. 31); "All Kinds of Kids" (p. 43)

Tercets (stanzas of three lines each): "Look for the Helpers" (p. 35); "Field Day Fun" (p. 91); "Clean Up" (p. 129)

Quatrains (stanzas of four lines each that often rhyme):
"Is Anybody Out There?" (p. 93): ABCB rhyme scheme
"The Most Glad-to-See Day of the Year" (p. 127): ABAB rhyme scheme

Unusual Forms:

Cuban Décima Mirror: Two redondillas with a bridge for an octosyllabic rhyme pattern (ABBA AA ABBA). "Secret Worlds" (p. 104).

Reverso: A "reverso" (a form invented by Marilyn Singer) consists of two stanzas (or two poems). The lines of the first stanza (or poem) are reversed in the second stanza (or poem) to give that stanza (or poem) a completely different meaning. "Principal for a Day" (p. 37).

Question and Answer: Two stanzas form a Q (Question) and A (Answer) dialogue between two points of view. "Head Lice Q&A" (p. 126).

Pledge Poem: Uses the language and rhythm of "The Pledge of Allegiance" as a model for a new "pledge" poem. "Let's Pledge Between Us" (p. 131).

Vivid Vocabulary: Poems can illustrate the concept of effective word choice quickly and powerfully.

"Virtual Adventure" (p. 113): geography words (*Katmandu, Serengeti, Beijing*), made-up words (*squid-eos*)
"Clean Up" (p. 129): *slipshod, slapdash*
"School Bake Sale" (p. 115): *slathered, bursting*, names of baked goods
"Cat Coder" (p. 67): *sashay, loop, bop*
"The World's Most Intelligent Chicken" (p. 118): *ibis, iris*

Incorporating Non-English Words: Sometimes poets use words from languages other than English for particular meaning or emphasis.

"How to Make a Friend" (p. 27); "Bilingual" (p. 97); "Bilingüe" (p. 98)

ABOUT THE TAKE 5! ACTIVITIES

Each poem in *The Poetry Friday Anthology* series includes a *Take 5!* mini-lesson that integrates skills instruction in a fun and meaningful context. While the content for each *Take 5!* mini-lesson is tailored to the individual poems, all *Take 5!* boxes contain the same sequence of tips for consistency and ease of use. These are only suggested activities and curriculum connections. Teachers can pick and choose what works best for them and for their students.

Tip #1: **READ ALOUD.** This tip provides an easy suggestion for how to make the poem come alive as you read it aloud by pairing the poem with a prop, adding gestures or movement, trying specific dramatic reading techniques, adding visuals or sound effects, and so on.

Tip #2: **READ TOGETHER.** This tip suggests how to engage children in reading the poem aloud with the teacher. For example, with echo reading children repeat certain words or lines after the teacher. Or the teacher might invite children to join in on repeated words or phrases.

Tip #3: DISCUSS. We provide a fun discussion question or quick oral activity tailored to fit the poem and to encourage diversity in responses. Here, we focus on connecting the poem with student experience and NOT on guessing one correct answer.

Tip #4: **SKILL FOCUS.** After reading the poem several times and discussing it briefly in the first three steps of the Take 5 activities, it's time to focus on one skill or cross-genre connection such as rhyme, rhythm, repetition, alliteration, personification, metaphor, simile, and so on—all identified and described for instant implementation.

Tip #5: **POEM CONNECTION.** This tip suggests related poem titles and poetry book titles that connect well with the featured poem for further enjoyment, connection, and possible comparison.

POEMS WITH TAKE 5! ACTIVITIES

You can find Take 5! *mini-lessons for the following poems in the books listed below. For more information on these titles in* The Poetry Friday Anthology *series, see* **Get "Poetry Plus" with *The Poetry Friday Anthology* Series** *on page 176.*

The Poetry Friday Anthology (K-5)

"The Most Glad-to-See Day of the Year" by Allan Wolf, p. 21
"My Kindergarten Choir" by Avis Harley, p. 42
"Photo Op" by Linda Sue Park, p. 82
"Skype" by Janet Wong, p. 90
"The Library" by Sara Holbrook, p. 107
"Recess" by Avis Harley, p. 108
"A Quiet Day" by Amy Ludwig VanDerwater, p. 174
"Poem for a Bully" by Eileen Spinelli, p. 208
"The World's Most Intelligent Chicken" by Jack Prelutsky, p. 227

The Poetry Friday Anthology for Middle School

"Giving" by Jane Yolen, p. 57
"Who Am I?" by Margarita Engle, p. 141
"Food Fest" by Heidi Bee Roemer, p. 199

The Poetry Friday Anthology for Science

"Recycling" by Susan Blackaby, p. 88
"My Experiment" by Julie Larios, p. 114
"Science Fair" by Eric Ode, p. 178
"What Is Science?" by Cynthia Cotten, p. 189
"Virtual Adventure" by Renée M. LaTulippe, p. 215

The Poetry Friday Anthology for Celebrations

"New Year Is Here" by Kenn Nesbitt, p. 29
"Compliment Chain" by Mary Lee Hahn, p. 45
"Bilingual"/"Bilingüe" by Alma Flor Ada, pp. 66-67
"Sincerely" by Robyn Hood Black, p. 79
"STOP! Let's Read" by Kristy Dempsey, p. 115
"Selfie" by Lorie Ann Grover, p. 131
"Bicycle Dreams" by Michael Salinger, p. 133
"Let's Go" by Merry Bradshaw, p. 135
"Look for the Helpers" by Michelle Heidenrich Barnes, p. 143
"Things Not to Do" by Eileen Spinelli, p. 149
"How to Make a Friend" by Jane Heitman Healy, p. 203
"No Kidding" by Michelle Schaub, p. 223
"Make a Joyful Noise" by B.J. Lee, p. 263
"Beep, Beep, Beep!" by Suzy Levinson, p. 265
"At Our House" by Virginia Euwer Wolff, p. 287
"Winter Counting" by Joseph Bruchac, p. 309
"Friends" by Renée M. LaTulippe, p. 313

TAKE 5! MINI-LESSON EXAMPLE #1

Here is an explanation of the *Take 5!* mini-lesson as it is used in *The Poetry Friday Anthology* (K-5) and *The Poetry Friday Anthology for Middle School* (grades 6-8), available in both Common Core and Texas TEKS versions with **skill connections for every poem.** The *Take 5!* mini-lesson in *The Poetry Friday Anthology for Science* (K-5) is similar except that Tip #4 highlights a science skill instead of a language arts (poetry) skill.

THIS IS THE TAKE 5! FOR "PHOTO OP" BY LINDA SUE PARK. FIND THIS POEM ON P. 29.

Photo Op
by Linda Sue Park

"Get together, look this way.
Lean in—you'll have to squeeze.
That's it—that's good, just stay right there.
And one-two-three—say CHEESE!"

Can someone tell me why it is
we have to holler "cheese"?
Just once I'd like a photo snapped
while everyone yells "FLEAS!"

Poem copyright © 2012 by Linda Sue Park;
Take 5! copyright © 2012 by Pomelo Books
from *The Poetry Friday Anthology* (K-5);
pages 15, 82

1
Pose the class together for an **informal group photograph** taken with your camera, phone, or tablet. Read this poem aloud before you snap the photo. Say *FLEAS!*

2
Invite the students to **join in on saying *CHEESE!* and *FLEAS!*** Alert them to the poet's use of all capital letters for greater emphasis and a cue to their reading.

3
For discussion: *What makes a school or family photo funny?*

4
The poet uses capital letters **to indicate when words should receive greater emphasis** (*CHEESE!, FLEAS!*). Guide the students in discussing this choice and contrast it with the impact of the words in lowercase (*cheese, fleas*).

5
Another occasion that often calls for photos is a choir performance such as the one depicted in **"My Kindergarten Choir" by Avis Harley.**

TAKE 5! MINI-LESSON EXAMPLE #2

Here is an explanation of the *Take 5!* mini-lesson as it is used in *The Poetry Friday Anthology for Celebrations* (K-8). Here, **each poem is matched with a recent, relevant picture book** to make a cross-genre connection (fiction/poetry). In addition, a skills matrix identifying reading/language arts skills and social studies skills for each poem is also provided.

1
Set the stage by **asking children if they have ever experienced help in an emergency** or seen it depicted on TV. Then read this poem aloud slowly.

2
Share the poem again and **invite children to chime in on the important last two lines** (*A person / Who cares*) as you read the whole poem aloud.

3
Talk about **what the Red Cross does** (help people during emergencies). A helpful resource is IFRC.org.

4
Pair this poem with the picture book *Clara and Davie* by Patricia Polacco (Scholastic, 2014), which is about American Red Cross founder Clara Barton and the brother who helped her realize her "gift for healing." Then brainstorm ways that children can be helpers and healers.

5
Link with **another poem about helping,** "Box for the Thrift Shop" by April Halprin Wayland (August, pages 224-225), and with poem selections from *Lend a Hand* by John Frank.

THIS IS THE TAKE 5! FOR "LOOK FOR THE HELPERS" BY MICHELLE H. BARNES. FIND THIS POEM ON P. 35.

Look for the Helpers
by Michelle Heidenrich Barnes

Look for the helpers
The healers
The givers

The arms-open
Hand-holding
Everyday heroes

The ones who bring food
Extra clothes
And first aid

Who offer safe shelter
A roof
And a bed

Follow their lead
Be a hugger
A helper

A friend who will listen
A person
Who cares

POETRY PERFORMANCE TIPS

It can be fun to read these poems aloud using simple theater and performance tips to make your poetry readings more memorable.

Simple props can add fun to sharing a poem with a group or larger audience. Use a common object mentioned in the poem as a "poetry prop" and hold it up while reading aloud. For example, bring a penny, nickel, dime, quarter, and/or dollar to use as a poetry prop when reading "Walking for a Cause" (page 79).

Adding motions or pantomime while you read a poem aloud can make a poem more engaging. Often it's possible to act out the words of a poem. For example, read aloud "Recess" (page 55) and add motions for playing soccer, running races, quietly reading, finding leaves, and playing chess.

Poems that have a repeated line or phrase can be fun to read together. For example, "Time for Lunch" (page 25) has a repeated line that everyone can chime in on (*Single file. Silent feet.*). While one person reads most of the poem aloud, everyone can join in on the repeated line.

Echo reading is another way to read a poem aloud with a group. One person says each line of the poem, pausing after each line so the rest of the group can repeat the line. Poems with short lines work best.

Consider using audio sound effects or music as a backdrop for a poem reading, where appropriate. Two great sources of sounds and sound effects are SoundCloud.com and the app Novel Effect (see NovelEffect.com), which features several poems from *The Poetry Friday Anthology* series, including "Make a Joyful Noise" by B.J. Lee (page 65).

A poem that employs **italicized text can be the perfect opportunity for an interactive read-aloud,** with a leader or narrator reading most of the poem and others reading the italicized text for added emphasis.

Invite guest readers to join you for the oral reading of a poem to add vocal variety. For example, invite the librarian to read aloud "The Library" (page 73) or invite a Spanish speaker to read "Bilingüe" aloud in Spanish (page 98).

SETTING THE STAGE FOR POETRY

Creating an environment that values poetry depends partly on the physical arrangement of space and materials and partly on the emotional climate that is established. Consider these common poetry practices below as well as the poetry books in the classroom, school, or library. (For more guidance on selecting, evaluating, and sharing poetry with children, check out *The Poetry Teacher's Book of Lists* by Sylvia Vardell).

1. Use poetry posters and poetry book displays to create a welcoming environment around the school.

2. Post poems in unexpected places, such as the front office, near the water fountain, or on a shelf, table, desk, chalk rail, wagon, or other prominent place.

3. Feature children's poets, poems, and poetry books in exhibits, promotional materials, book talks, and newsletters.

4. At staff meetings, invite teachers or the librarian to highlight new poetry books, overlooked poetry book gems, books by featured poets, and children's favorite poetry books.

5. Encourage incorporating poetry across the curriculum in language arts, social studies, science, mathematics, and physical education.

6. Make plans to celebrate National Poetry Month and Poem in Your Pocket Day (both in April) by putting free poems in a basket in the front office.

7. Be sure the library has plenty of poetry on the shelves, including newly published titles and award winners, with multiple copies of current and popular titles and room for expansion.

8. Leave a copy of this book in the teachers' lounge for browsing!

POETRY ACROSS THE CURRICULUM

On a practical level, **poetry collections can also serve the school curriculum well.** Poetry has many teaching and pedagogical uses across the curriculum—for building science concepts, reinforcing historical themes, adding motivation to math lessons, as a "sponge" activity in transition times, and so on.

When it comes to supporting instruction across the curriculum, poetry offers these distinct advantages:

- Poetry is accessible to a **wide range of reading abilities**.

- The brief format of much poetry **taps the essence of a subject.**

- Poetry incorporates **sensory language**, giving children the sense of touching, tasting, smelling, hearing, and seeing.

- Poetry can make a topic memorable through the use of **vivid imagery.**

- Poetry can provide a vehicle for content presented through evocative language and **rich vocabulary.**

- Poetry can help children **talk about issues** that concern them.

We can add poetry sharing to a planned content area lesson by taking one minute to read aloud a relevant poem to set the stage for the instruction to come. Or conversely, ending with a poem can help reinforce the concepts introduced in a lesson by building knowledge retention so crucial to learning.

Using poetry across the curriculum by starting a lesson with a themed or topical poem can show children how writers approach topics in very different and distinctive ways. In addition, **children will see that they can learn a lot of information from a poem**. Poetry has an advantage in that it typically consists of fewer words than expository prose passages. Poems can be read and reread in very little time. Each rereading can be approached in a slightly different way—for example, through choral reading or poetry performance—and offer closure to a lesson or extend it further.

Naturally, a single poem is not intended to be an entire content area lesson, but it offers an innovative, engaging, vocabulary-full, and concept-rich way to launch or conclude a lesson. Jill Castek challenges us to **"break down those instructional silos"** and look for opportunities to maximize overlap. We need to ensure that vocabulary exposure is occurring in many contexts for maximum scaffolding and learning.

POETRY AWARDS

There are several major awards given to poets and works of poetry. Knowing about these awards can help you keep up with what is considered high-quality work.

POETS

The **Young People's Poet Laureate** (YPPL) recognizes a poet for her/his body of work. The YPPL consults with the Poetry Foundation and raises awareness of the power of poetry for young people.

The **National Council of Teachers of English (NCTE) Award for Excellence in Poetry for Children** is given to a poet for an entire body of work in writing or anthologizing poetry for children.

The **Lee Bennett Hopkins/ILA Promising Poet Award** goes to a poet with one or two published books, and aims to encourage new poets.

POETRY BOOKS

The Lee Bennett Hopkins Award for Children's Poetry (given annually by Penn State University)

The Claudia Lewis Award (given annually by Bank Street College)

The Lion and the Unicorn Award for Excellence in North American Poetry in either the U.S. or Canada

The CYBILS Award (Children's & Young Adult Bloggers' Literary Awards)

BOOKLISTS

The NCTE Excellence in Poetry Award Committee selects a list of **NCTE Poetry Notables** including both poetry books and verse novels.

The CL/R SIG of the International Literacy Association selects **Notable Books for a Global Society** for enhancing understanding of world cultures and includes poetry.

POETRY BOOKS FOR LEADERS

Whether it's the day of an assembly, a parents' meeting, an unusual holiday, or another occasion, sharing a poem can make for a memorable moment. Here is a selection of poetry books for children about a variety of celebrations and occasions.

Bagert, Brod. 2008. *School Fever.* *Hilarious poems about school from the child's point of view

Dakos, Kalli. 2003. *Put Your Eyes Up Here: And Other School Poems.* *Fun, lively poems that explore the world of one make-believe classroom

Derby, Sally. 2017. *A New School Year.* *Six children (K-5) share their worries, hopes, and successes on the first day of school

Florian, Douglas. 2018. *Friends and Foes: Poems About Us All.* *Humorous and honest poems about the many facets of friendship

Franco, Betsy. 2009. *Messing Around the Monkey Bars and Other School Poems for Two Voices.* *Playful poems that capture life around the school from the playground to the library to the classroom

Heard, Georgia. Ed. 2002. *This Place I Know: Poems of Comfort.* * Eighteen illustrated poems for times of crisis

Hopkins, Lee Bennett. Ed. 2005. *Days to Celebrate: A Full Year of Poetry, People, Holidays, History, Fascinating Facts, and More.* *Poems for every month of the year including holidays, historic events, and so on

Hopkins, Lee Bennett. Ed. 2018. *School People.* *An anthology that celebrates the grown-ups that children encounter throughout the school day

Janeczko, Paul. Ed. 2014. *Firefly July: A Year of Very Short Poems.* *Thirty-six very short poems that cross the seasons of the year

Kennedy, Caroline. Ed. 2013. *Poems to Learn by Heart.* * 100+ poems grouped by theme on self, family, sports, school, and more

Lewis, J. Patrick. 2009. *Countdown to Summer: A Poem for Every Day of the School Year.* *Fun poetry full of wordplay on a variety of subjects and forms that counts down from the first day of school to the last

Lewis, J. Patrick. Ed. 2012. *National Geographic Book of Animal Poetry.*
    *The world of animals (on land, in the sea, in the air, big and little,
    quiet and noisy) brought to life in 200+ poems

Lewis, J. Patrick. Ed. 2015. *National Geographic Book of Nature Poetry.*
    *200+ exuberant poems in a variety of voices, capturing the
    awesomeness of nature along with stunning photographs

Lewis, J. Patrick. 2018. *The Poetry of US: More than 200 Poems about the
    People, Places, and Passions of the United States.* *200+ poems
    and photographs featuring America's people and places

Prelutsky, Jack. Ed. 2010. *There's No Place Like School.* *Fun poems about
    the highs and lows of school life

Raczka, Bob. 2010. *Guyku: A Year of Haiku for Boys.* *Haiku poems about
    outdoor fun through the seasons from a boy's point of view

Salas, Laura Purdie. 2009. *Stampede! Poems to Celebrate the Wild Side of
    School!* *An inventive poetry collection featuring first- and second-
    graders at school

Shields, Carol Diggory. 2003. *Almost Late to School: And More School
    Poems.* *Lighthearted poetry that explores a broad range of
    school-based events

Sidman, Joyce. 2013. *What the Heart Knows: Chants, Charms & Blessings.*
    *Poems that provide courage, comfort, and humor at difficult or
    daunting moments in life

Singer, Marilyn. 2012. *Every Day's a Dog's Day: A Year in Poems.* *The
    dog's point of view on major human holidays as well as dog
    "holidays" such as Hole Digging Day or Visit to the Vet Day

VanDerwater, Amy Ludwig. 2017. *Read! Read! Read!* *23 poems about the
    joy of reading everything from maps to sports news

Winters, Kay. 2018. *Did You Hear What I Heard? Poems about School.* *35
    poems about a variety of elementary school experiences

Yolen, Jane and Peters, Andrew Fusek. Eds. 2007. *Here's a Little Poem: A
    Very First Book of Poetry.* *More than sixty poems for very young
    children about enjoying the adventures of the day

POETRY BLOGS & WEBSITES

There are many excellent poetry-related websites and blogs to explore, with poems, information about poets, sample poems and activities, tips and games, and much more. Here are some of our favorite sites.

The Academy of American Poets
Poets.org
*National organization that promotes poets and the art of poetry

Alphabet Soup
by Jama Rattigan
JamaRattigan.com
*Features food-related literature

Colorín Colorado
ColorinColorado.org
*Resource for educators and families of English language learners (ELLs)

Favorite Poem Project
FavoritePoem.org
*Poems chosen and read by regular people

Giggle Poetry
GigglePoetry.com
*Poems and activities, games, and poem scripts

The Miss Rumphius Effect
by Tricia Stohr-Hunt
MissRumphiusEffect.Blogspot.com
*Reviews children's poetry and nonfiction

Novel Effect
NovelEffect.com
*Theme music and sound effects for reading books and poems aloud

Pinterest/PomeloBooks
Pinterest.com/PomeloBooks.com
*Visual "postcards" feature poems

Poetry Alive
PoetryAlive.com
*Offers high-energy poetry performances

Poetry Celebrations
PoetryCelebrations.com
*Additional material, such as audio clips and video links, to accompany *The Poetry Friday Anthology for Celebrations*

Poetry for Children
by Sylvia Vardell
PoetryForChildren.Blogspot.com
*Comprehensive resource of info about sharing poetry

Poetry Foundation Children's Page
Poetryfoundation.org/resources/children
*Hundreds of poems and interesting articles

The Poetry Minute
PoetryMinute.org
*Poems for the whole school year

SoundCloud
SoundCloud.com
*Audio platform to upload, record, promote and share original sounds

A Year of Reading
by Franki Sibberson & Mary Lee Hahn
ReadingYear.Blogspot.com
*Two teachers share ideas and resources for teaching with literature

POET BLOGS

Many poets keep and update regular blogs with helpful information about sharing, reading, writing, and even revising poetry.

April Halprin Wayland
TeachingAuthors.com

Beyond LiteracyLink
by Carol Varsalona
BeyondLiteracyLink.blogspot.com

Buffy's Blog
by Buffy Silverman
BuffySilverman.com/blog

Caroline Starr Rose Blog
by Caroline Starr Rose
CarolineStarrRose.com/blog

David L. Harrison's Blog
DavidLHarrison.Wordpress.com

The Drift Record
by Julie Larios
JulieLarios.blogspot.com

Elizabeth Steinglass Blog
by Elizabeth Steinglass
ElizabethSteinglass.com/blog

Eric Ode Blog
by Eric Ode
EricOde.com/blog

Gottabook
by Greg Pincus
GottaBook.blogspot.com

HATBOOKS
by Holly Thompson
Hatbooks.blogspot.com

Laura Shovan Blog
by Laura Shovan
LauraShovan.com/blog

Life on the Deckle Edge
by Robyn Hood Black
RobynHoodBlack.com/blog

Michelle Schaub Blog
by Michelle Schaub
MichelleSchaub.com/blog

No Water River
by Renée M. LaTulippe
NoWaterRiver.com

Poetrepository
by Mary Lee Hahn
MaryLeeHahn.com

The Poem Farm
by Amy Ludwig VanDerwater
PoemFarm.AmyLV.com

Poetry for Kids
by Kenn Nesbitt
Poetry4Kids.com

Reading to the Core
by Catherine Flynn
ReadingtotheCore.wordpress.com

Read, Learn and Be Happy
by Jane Heitman Healy
ReadLearnandBeHappy.blogspot.com

Today's Little Ditty
by Michelle Heidenrich Barnes
MichelleHBarnes.blogspot.com

Wild Rose Reader
by Elaine Magliaro
WiildRoseReader.blogspot.com

Write Time
by Linda Kulp Trout
LindaKulpTrout.blogspot.com

Writing the World for Kids
by Laura Purdie Salas
LauraSalas.com/blog

NURTURING YOUNG WRITERS

Several poets have written books ABOUT poetry writing for young people. Here are a few that might be helpful.

Holbrook, Sara, Salinger, Michael, and Harvey, Stephanie. 2018. *From Striving to Thriving Writers: Strategies that Jump-Start Writing.* *Twenty-seven writing strategies and lessons targeting reading, writing, and speaking

Lawson, JonArno. 2008. *Inside Out: Children's Poets Discuss Their Work.* *Twenty-three poets sharing poems and explaining how the poem came to be

Prelutsky, Jack. 2008. *Pizza, Pigs, and Poetry: How to Write a Poem.* *The poet sharing how he creates poems from anecdotes, often using comic exaggeration

Salas, Laura Purdie. 2011. *Picture Yourself Writing Poetry: Using Photos to Inspire Writing.* *A clear and engaging approach with writing prompts and mentor texts

Meet the Author series
Look for picture books in the "Meet the Author" series. Here, poets like Douglas Florian, Lee Bennett Hopkins, Karla Kuskin, Janet Wong, and Jane Yolen talk about their lives and how they write poetry. These are published by Richard C. Owen Publishers.

Here are several notable books with poetry written BY young people.

Lowe, Ayana. Ed. 2008. *Come and Play: Children of Our World Having Fun.* *Photos of children around the world along with poems by young writers, ages 5-11

Lyne, Sandford. Ed. 2004. *Soft Hay Will Catch You.* *Poems by young writers about home and family, gathered by Kentucky poet Lyne

Nye, Naomi Shihab. Ed. 2000. *Salting the Ocean: 100 Poems by Young Poets.* *"100 poems by 100 poets in grades one through twelve," collected by Nye

Rogé. 2014. *Haiti My Country: Poems by Haitian Schoolchildren.* *Close-up painted portraits of real kids in Haiti, accompanied by their brief personal poems

Spain, Sahara Sunday. 2001. *If There Would Be No Light: Poems from My Heart.* *Poems by a nine-year-old who has traveled the world

PLACES FOR STUDENTS TO PUBLISH POETRY

Here are several different print and online sources that publish poetry by young writers. Be sure to check the rules before submitting any writing to each place. Have students give it a try—and remind them that even Dr. Seuss and J.K. Rowling received many rejection letters before being published!

Canvas (ages 8-13)
CanvasLiteraryJournal.com
*Published in print, ebook, web, video, and audio formats

Carus Publishing
(*Cicada, Cobblestone, Faces, Dig, Muse*) (ages 9-14+)
CobblestonePub.com/index.html
*Magazines on topics from nature to history and more

Creative Kids
CKMagazine.org
*"The nation's largest magazine for and by kids"

New Moon: The Magazine for Girls and Their Dreams
NewMoon.com
*A special online community and magazine for girls

River of Words (ages 5-19)
StMarys-ca.edu/center-for-environmental-literacy/river-of-words
Center or Environmental Literacy (Saint Mary's College of California)
*A youth poetry and art contest to inspire children to translate their observations into creative expression

Skipping Stones
SkippingStones.org
*An international, multicultural, environmental magazine

Stone Soup
StoneSoup.com
*Stories, poems, book reviews, and artwork by young people

The Telling Room (ages 6-18)
TellingRoom.org/stories
*Publications of annual anthologies, chapbooks, and web content

A LETTER TO PARENTS

Get families on board as literacy partners with this note that you can copy and paste into your weekly newsletter. (Also find it at PomeloBooks.com as a document that you can customize for your school community.)

Dear Families:

This year we're adding something new to our morning announcements: POETRY! In a few minutes a day, we hope to use poems to support our school culture of kindness, safety, respect, and gratitude.

The resource that we will be drawing inspiration from is *GREAT Morning! Poems for School Leaders to Read Aloud* by Sylvia Vardell and Janet Wong (Pomelo Books). Ask our librarian if you can borrow a copy of this book from our library—and continue the discussions at home. Here is a selection from that book to encourage family reading at any time of day, any day of the week.

At Our House
by Virginia Euwer Wolff

Dad reads to me while he makes me lunch,
Mom reads to me in bed.
My little brother wants to hear
every word that we have read.

Grandpa's learning how to read,
Grandma hums along.
Books speak right up in our house,
and words turn into song.

Poem copyright © 2015 by Virginia Euwer Wolff
GREAT Morning! Poems for School Leaders to Read Aloud
by Sylvia Vardell & Janet Wong (Pomelo Books)

Very truly yours,

SHARING POETRY AT HOME

Here are a dozen simple ways for families to include poetry in the daily routine at home, from sharing a poem at breakfast to recording a favorite poem for a friend or family member far away.

- Start the day with a poem at breakfast
- Add a poem to a lunch bag
- Keep a book of poetry in the car and take turns reading out loud
- Look for poems on your cell phone or tablet when waiting
- Celebrate each birthday with a special poem
- Write a poem on the sidewalk with chalk
- Listen online to poems performed by the poets
- Write a poem together as a gift for a special occasion
- Record a poem to share with a friend or family member far away
- Listen to songs on the radio and talk about how they are alike or different from poetry
- Just for fun, sing a silly poem together
- End the day with a poem at dinner or at bedtime

WHEN THERE IS TEAMWORK AND COLLABORATION, WONDERFUL THINGS CAN BE ACHIEVED.

MATTIE STEPANEK

INDEXES
&
CREDITS

SUBJECT INDEX

TITLE INDEX

POET INDEX

POEM CREDITS

Each of the poems listed below is used with the permission of the author. To request reprint rights, please write us at info@pomelobooks.com and we will put you in touch with the poets. Note: Some of these poems were first published in another *Poetry Friday Anthology* book. You can find them there with different mini-lessons and supplemental materials.

PFA = *The Poetry Friday Anthology*
PFAMS = *The Poetry Friday Anthology for Middle School*
PFAC = *The Poetry Friday Anthology for Celebrations*
PFAS = *The Poetry Friday Anthology for Science*

Alma Flor Ada: "Bilingual"/"Bilingüe"; © 2015 by Alma Flor Ada. **PFAC**

Brod Bagert: "Is Anybody Out There?"; © 2018 by Brod Bagert.

Michelle Heidenrich Barnes: "Look for the Helpers"; © 2015 by Michelle Heidenrich Barnes. **PFAC**

Robyn Hood Black: "Sincerely"; © 2015 by Robyn Hood Black. **PFAC**

Susan Blackaby: "Recycling"; © 2014 by Susan Blackaby. **PFAS**

Merry Bradshaw: "Let's Go"; © 2015 by Merry Bradshaw. **PFAC**

Lydia Breiseth: "In the Life of a Substitute"; © 2018 by Lydia Breiseth.

Joseph Bruchac: "Winter Counting"; © 2015 by Joseph Bruchac. **PFAC**. "Your Teacher"; © 2018 by Joseph Bruchac.

Kate Coombs: "The House of This Minute"; © 2018 by Kate Coombs.

Cynthia Cotten: "What Is Science?"; © 2014 by Cynthia Cotten. **PFAS**

Kristy Dempsey: "STOP! Let's Read"; © 2015 by Kristy Dempsey. **PFAC**

Margarita Engle: "Secret Worlds"; © 2018 by Margarita Engle. "Who Am I?"; © 2013 by Margarita Engle. **PFAMS**

Janet Clare Fagal: "Oh, Those Forms!"; © 2018 by Janet Clare Fagal.

Catherine Flynn: "Walking for a Cause"; © 2018 by Catherine Flynn.

Xelena González: "Testing Blues"; © 2018 by Xelena González.

Joan Bransfield Graham: "CELEBRATE!"; © 2018 by Joan Bransfield Graham.

Lorie Ann Grover: "Selfie"; © 2015 by Lorie Ann Grover. **PFAC**

Mary Lee Hahn: "Compliment Chain"; © 2015 by Mary Lee Hahn. **PFAC**

Avis Harley: "My Kindergarten Choir"; "Recess"; © 2012 by Avis Harley. **PFA**

Jane Heitman Healy: "How to Make a Friend"; © 2015 by Jane Heitman Healy. **PFAC**

Sara Holbrook: "The Library"; © 2012 by Sara Holbrook. **PFA**

Ann Ingalls: "Our Custodian"; © 2018 by Ann Ingalls.

Julie Larios: "My Experiment"; © 2014 by Julie Larios. **PFAS**

Renée M. LaTulippe: "Friends"; © 2015 by Renée M. LaTulippe. **PFAC**. "Virtual Adventure"; © 2014 by Renée M. LaTulippe. **PFAS**

B.J. Lee: "Make a Joyful Noise"; © 2015 by B.J. Lee. **PFAC**

Suzy Levinson: "Beep, Beep, Beep!"; © 2015 by Suzy Levinson. **PFAC**

Elaine Magliaro: "School Bake Sale"; © 2018 by Elaine Magliaro.

Kenn Nesbitt: "New Year Is Here"; © 2015 by Kenn Nesbitt. **PFAC**

ABOUT THE POETS

If you identified "favorite poets" when reading the poems in this anthology, contact them about speaking at your school or library—or participating in a conference or teacher inservice session. Poets' websites are listed here, where you can find their contact info, news about their books, and even links to their blogs.

Alma Flor Ada

AlmaFlorAda.com

Alma Flor Ada, Professor Emerita at the University of San Francisco, is the author of over one hundred books of poetry, folklore, narrative, and nonfiction, including *Yes! We Are Latinos,* co-written with F. Isabel Campoy. Her books have received numerous awards.

Brod Bagert

BrodBagert.com

Brod Bagert, a native of New Orleans, started his career as a poet in third grade with a poem for his mother. Now the author of nearly two dozen books of poetry, including *Shout! Little Poems that Roar,* Bagert is well known for his lively poetry performances.

Michelle Heidenrich Barnes

MichelleHBarnes.com

Michelle Heidenrich Barnes is from Florida and grew up obsessed with theatre, dance, and music. She publishes poetry in books, magazines, and on greeting cards, leads creative workshops, and keeps the blog *Today's Little Ditty.*

Robyn Hood Black

RobynHoodBlack.com

Robyn Hood Black grew up in Orlando, Florida, taught middle school English, and is the author of *Sir Mike* and *Wolves.* She also creates "literary art with a vintage vibe" through her business, ArtsyLetters.com.

Susan Blackaby

Susan Blackaby writes fiction and nonfiction for K-8, including leveled readers, chapter books, picture books, and poetry. Her book *Nest, Nook & Cranny,* a collection of animal "home poems," won the Lion and the Unicorn Award.

Merry Bradshaw

Merry Bradshaw, a writer and former educator, lives in Nevada. Her writing has been featured in children's books and National Geographic's Explorer Magazines. In addition, she is the author of *H is for Hummingbirds: Nature's Jewels.*

Lydia Breiseth

Lydia Breiseth is Director of Colorín Colorado, the nation's leading website serving educators and families of English language learners. She is the author of numerous articles, blog posts, and guides focused on education and literacy.

Joseph Bruchac

JosephBruchac.com

Joseph Bruchac has been writing poetry, short stories, novels, professional resources, and music reflecting his Abenaki Indian heritage and Native American traditions for over three decades. He has authored more than 120 books for children and adults.

Kate Coombs

KateCoombs.com

Kate Coombs is the author of several children's books, including poetry collections *Breathe and Be: A Book of Mindfulness Poems, Monster School,* and the award-winning *Water Sings Blue.* She lives in Utah.

Cynthia Cotten

CynthiaCotten.com

Cynthia Cotten is a widely anthologized poet and author of picture books, short stories, and novels, including *Snow Ponies* and *The Book Boat's In*. She lives in New York.

Kristy Dempsey

KristyDempsey.com

Kristy Dempsey is the author of *Me with You, Mini Racer, Surfer Chick, A Dance Like Starlight, Superhero Instruction Manual,* and more. She grew up in South Carolina, but now works as a teacher at The American School of Belo Horizonte in Brazil.

Margarita Engle

MargaritaEngle.com

Margarita Engle is the Poetry Foundation's 2017-19 Young People's Poet Laureate. She is the Cuban-American author of many picture books and verse novels, including the Newbery Honor winner *The Surrender Tree*.

Janet Clare Fagal

Janet Clare Fagal, poet and retired teacher, is an eager poetry advocate bringing poems and poets into the lives of children. Her award-winning poems appear in a variety of works, including a Lee Bennett Hopkins anthology.

Catherine Flynn

ReadingToTheCore.Wordpress.com

Catherine Flynn is a literacy specialist and recipient of a Teacher of the Year award for her district as well as a poet and poetry blogger. She lives in Connecticut.

Xelena González

AllAroundUs.info

Xelena González has been a librarian in an international school in China as well as a storyteller and author. Her debut book *All Around Us* received an American Indian Youth Literature Award Picture Book Honor, in addition to other awards and accolades.

Joan Bransfield Graham

JoanGraham.com

Joan Bransfield Graham is a picture book author and poet whose books include *The Poem that Will Not End: Fun with Poetic Forms and Voices*. An avid traveler and photographer, Joan enjoys visiting schools all over the world.

Lorie Ann Grover

LorieAnnGrover.Blogspot.com

Lorie Ann Grover is the author of middle grade verse novels, young adult novels, and board books, including *Loose Threads* (*Booklist* Top 10 Youth First Novel), *Firstborn*, and *Bedtime Kiss for Little Fish* (*Parents Magazine*'s 20 Best Children's Books.

Mary Lee Hahn

MaryLeeHahn.com

Mary Lee Hahn is a 5th grade teacher, poet, poetry blogger, literacy volunteer, and the author of *Reconsidering Read-Aloud* (Stenhouse), a professional book on read-aloud as a time when powerful, effective teaching and rigorous learning can take place.

Avis Harley

Avis Harley taught elementary school in England and Canada, and worked as a professor of education at the University of British Columbia. She is the author of several poetry collections, including *African Acrostics: A Word in Edgewise.*

Jane Heitman Healy

ReadLearnAndBeHappy.Blogspot.com

Jane Heitman Healy loves sharing poems with others of all ages. She has written three books for teachers and librarians as well as articles and short plays. A former teacher, she works at her local library in South Dakota.

Sara Holbrook

SaraHolbrook.com

Sara Holbrook is the author of more than a dozen books for children and adults. A frequent keynote speaker and performance poet, she shows teachers how to use writing and oral presentation exercises to raise vocabulary and other literacy skills.

Ann Ingalls

AnnIngallsWrites.com

Ann Ingalls passes the day exaggerating (writing fiction) or telling the truth (nonfiction). Her nearly 30 books for young readers include *J Is for Jazz, Biggety Bat: Hot Diggety!, Ice Cream Soup,* and *Fairy Floss: The Sweet Story of Cotton Candy.*

Julie Larios

JulieLarios.Blogspot.com

Julie Larios is a former faculty member in the Writing for Children MFA program at Vermont College of Fine Arts, the author of four books of poetry for children, including *Yellow Elephant: A Bright Bestiary,* and a winner of a Pushcart Prize.

Renée M. LaTulippe

ReneeLaTulippe.com

Renée M. LaTulippe has co-authored nine leveled readers, and her poetry appears in many anthologies. She teaches an online writing course, The Lyrical Language Lab, and blogs at *No Water River*. She lives in Italy with her husband and children.

B.J. Lee

ChildrensAuthorBJLee.com

B.J. Lee, a former librarian at The Boston Conservatory at Berklee, is now a full-time writer with many poems in anthologies and a forthcoming picture book, *There Was an Old Gator Who Swallowed a Moth.* She lives in Florida.

Suzy Levinson

SuzyLevinson.com

Suzy Levinson has had poems published in several anthologies, including *The Poetry Friday Anthology for Celebrations*. Other poems have appeared (or are forthcoming) in the *SCBWI Bulletin*, *Ladybug*, and *Highlights' High Five* and *Hello* magazines.

Elaine Magliaro

WildRoseReader.Blogspot.com

Elaine Magliaro was an elementary school teacher and librarian for more than three decades. Awards for her book *Things to Do!* include the Margaret Wise Brown Award and the Ezra Jack Keats New Writer Honor.

Kenn Nesbitt

Poetry4Kids.com

Kenn Nesbitt, Children's Poet Laureate (2013-15), is known for his funny poems and the online "poetry playground" that he created at Poetry4kids.com. His anthology *One Minute Till Bedtime: 60-Second Poems to Send You Off to Sleep* features poems by many poets included in this book.

Eric Ode

EricOde.com

Eric Ode (pronounced OH-dee), a former elementary teacher, is an author, poet, singer, and songwriter. He lives in Washington State and has written books about the Pacific Coast, pirates, cowboys, and wetlands, including *Sea Star Wishes*.

Linda Sue Park

LSPark.com

Linda Sue Park, Newbery-winning author of the novel *A Single Shard*, also writes picture books and poetry. Her first published work was a haiku, sold for a dollar to a magazine when she was nine years old; her dad still has that check.

Ann Whitford Paul

AnnWhitfordPaul.com

Ann Whitford Paul was inspired to write picture books after years of bedtime reading to her four children. Her publications include *If Animals Kissed Goodnight*. She is also the author of *Writing Picture Books: A Hands-On Guide from Story Creation to Publication*.

Greg Pincus

GregPincus.com

Greg Pincus, author of the novels *The Homework Strike* and *The 14 Fibs of Gregory K.*, is also a poet, screenwriter, volunteer elementary school librarian, social media consultant, and blogger writing about children's literature and poetry at *Gottabook*.

Jack Prelutsky

JackPrelutsky.com

Jack Prelutsky was the nation's first Children's Poet Laureate, selected by the Poetry Foundation in 2006. Author of *The New Kid on the Block* and more than 70 collections of poetry, he has also compiled anthologies such as *The 20th Century Children's Poetry Treasury*.

Bob Raczka

BobRaczka.com

Bob Raczka has worked in advertising, created a series of art appreciation books, and written several collections of poetry, including *Wet Cement: A Mix of Concrete Poems*. A message he shares with kids is "Make stuff!"

Heidi Bee Roemer

HeidiBRoemer.com

Heidi Bee Roemer is the author of four books, including *What Kinds of Seeds Are These?,* a riddle-based picture book presenting information about plants. Her poems have appeared in more than three dozen magazines, journals, and anthologies.

Caroline Starr Rose

CarolineStarrRose.com

Caroline Starr Rose is an award-winning middle grade and picture book author whose books have been nominated for many state award lists. She spent her childhood in Saudi Arabia and New Mexico, where she now lives with her husband and two sons.

Laura Purdie Salas

LauraSalas.com

Former teacher Laura Purdie Salas has written more than 125 books for kids, including *Meet My Family!*, the *Can Be...* series (Bank Street Best Books, IRA Teachers' Choice), *BookSpeak!* (NCTE Notable), and *If You Were the Moon*.

Michael Salinger

MichaelSalinger.com

Michael Salinger is a fixture in the performance poetry and education community, performing and teaching in over 200 cities in 35 countries. His publications include a collection of poems on vocabulary words, *Well Defined: Vocabulary in Rhyme*.

Darren Sardelli

DarrenSardelli.com

Award-winning author Darren Sardelli writes poems that teach and inspire. He's been published in over 20 poetry anthologies in the U.S. and U.K. as well as dozens of textbooks worldwide. Darren has visited more than 600 schools.

Liz Garton Scanlon

LizGartonScanlon.com

Liz Garton Scanlon is the author of more than a dozen beloved picture books and a middle grade novel. She is on the faculty of the Vermont College of Fine Arts and is a frequent and popular presenter at schools, festivals, and conferences.

Michelle Schaub

MichelleSchaub.com

Michelle Schaub is a teacher and children's poet from Downers Grove, Illinois. She is the author of the picture book poetry collections *Fresh-Picked Poetry: A Day at the Farmers' Market* and *Finding Treasure: A Collection of Collections*.

Laura Shovan
LauraShovan.com
Laura Shovan grew up in a family with New York, British, and Thai influences. She taught high school and worked as a journalist. Her novel in verse, *The Last Fifth Grade of Emerson Elementary*, has won multiple awards.

Buffy Silverman
BuffySilverman.com
Buffy Silverman is the author of 90 nonfiction books for children, featuring topics from angel sharks to alligators and Mars to monster trucks. Her nature-inspired poetry appears in popular anthologies and children's magazines.

Traci Sorell
TraciSorell.com
Traci Sorell grew up immersed in stories and accounts of her Cherokee ancestors' lives. She is the author of two picture books: *We Are Grateful: Otsaliheliga*, grounded in modern Cherokee culture, and *At the Mountain's Base*, a circular story in verse.

Eileen Spinelli
EileenSpinelli.com
Eileen Spinelli grew up in Pennsylvania and began writing at the age of six. She has written more than 70 children's books and poetry collections, including *Peace Week in Miss Fox's Class, Another Day as Emily,* and *Somebody Loves You, Mr. Hatch*.

Elizabeth Steinglass
ElizabethSteinglass.com
Elizabeth Steinglass lives in Washington, DC with her husband and two children. Her poetry has appeared in magazines and in *The Poetry Friday Anthology for Celebrations*. Her book *Soccer Nonsense* is forthcoming from Boyds Mills Press.

Holly Thompson
HATBooks.com
Holly Thompson is author of the verse novels *Falling into the Dragon's Mouth, The Language Inside,* and *Orchards.* Her picture books include the lyrical *Twilight Chant* and *One Wave at a Time,* and *The Wakame Gatherers.*

Linda Kulp Trout
LindaKulpTrout.Blogspot.com
Linda Kulp Trout has taught preschool, elementary, and middle school reading and language arts. She is now retired from teaching and spends her days writing for children and young adults.

Amy Ludwig VanDerwater
AmyLudwigVanDerwater.com
Amy Ludwig VanDerwater, a popular speaker, is the author of poetry, picture books, and professional books for teachers, including *With My Hands: Poems about Making Things* and *Poems Are Teachers: How Studying Poetry Strengthens Writing in All Genres.*

Carol Varsalona

BeyondLiteracyLink.Blogspot.com

Carol Varsalona is an English Language Arts consultant, moderator of #NYEDChat, Wonder Lead Ambassador for Wonderopolis, blogger, writer/poet, and creator of the online "Reflect with Me Galleries of Artistic Expressions."

April Halprin Wayland

AprilWayland.com

April Halprin Wayland grew up in California and has traveled through Europe. Now she writes for young people and teaches writing. She has authored a novel in verse and several picture books, including *More than Enough: A Passover Story.*

Carole Boston Weatherford

CBWeatherford.com

Carole Boston Weatherford is a Professor of English at Fayetteville State University in North Carolina. Her award-winning work celebrates African American experiences and includes *Schomburg: The Man Who Built a Library* and many others.

Kay Winters

KayWinters.com

Kay Winters was a classroom teacher, reading specialist, and college instructor. She is a frequent presenter at schools and has 24 books published for students, the newest being *Did You Hear What I Heard? Poems about School.*

Allan Wolf

AllanWolf.com

Allan Wolf is a poet, presenter, and author of picture books, poetry, and YA historical novels. His next book of space poems, *The Day the Universe Exploded My Head!*, is due out in 2019 to celebrate the 50th anniversary of the landing on the moon!

Virginia Euwer Wolff

VirginiaEuwerWolff.com

A former teacher, Virginia Euwer Wolff is the author of the *Make Lemonade* series for young adults. Other acclaimed titles by Wolff are *The Mozart Season, Probably Still Nick Swansen*, and *Bat 6*, winner of the Jane Addams Peace Award.

Janet Wong

JanetWong.com

Janet Wong is the author of more than 30 books, including the poetry collections *Knock on Wood: Poems about Superstitions* and *Twist: Yoga Poems.*

Jane Yolen

JaneYolen.com

Jane Yolen is today's most prolific and versatile writer for young people, writing everything from picture books to fantasy and science fiction novels. She is also a teacher of writing and has been called the Hans Christian Andersen of America.

ABOUT VARDELL AND WONG

Sylvia M. Vardell is Professor in the School of Library and Information Studies at Texas Woman's University and teaches graduate courses in children's and young adult literature. Vardell has published extensively, including five books on literature for children as well as over 25 book chapters and 100 journal articles. Her current work focuses on poetry for children, including a regular blog, *PoetryforChildren.Blogspot.com*. Vardell has served as a member or chair of several national award committees, including the NCTE Award for Poetry, the ALA Odyssey Award, and the Sibert, the Wilder, and the Caldecott award committees, among others. She has conducted over 150 presentations at state, regional, national, and international conferences. She taught at the University of Zimbabwe in Africa as a Fulbright scholar and is the 2014 recipient of the Scholastic Library Publishing Award.

Janet Wong is a graduate of Yale Law School and a former lawyer who switched careers to become a children's author. Her dramatic career change has been featured on *The Oprah Winfrey Show*, CNN's *Paula Zahn Show*, and *Radical Sabbatical*. She is the author of more than 30 books for children and teens on a wide variety of subjects, including writing and revision (*You Have to Write*), diversity and community (*Apple Pie 4th of July*), peer pressure (*Me and Rolly Maloo*), chess (*Alex and the Wednesday Chess Club*), and yoga (*Twist: Yoga Poems*). A frequent featured speaker at literacy conferences, Wong has served as a member of several national committees, including the NCTE Poetry Committee and the ILA Notable Books for a Global Society committee. Her current focus is encouraging children to publish their own writing using affordable new technologies.

Together, **Vardell & Wong** are the creative forces behind *The Poetry Friday Anthology* series and the *Poetry Friday Power Book* series. You can learn more about their books at **PomeloBooks.com.**

GET "POETRY PLUS"
WITH THE POETRY FRIDAY ANTHOLOGY® SERIES!

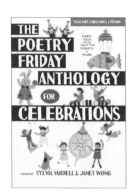

The Poetry Friday Anthology for Celebrations
ILA 2016 Notable Books for a Global Society

Teacher/Librarian Edition (K-8)
Each of the 156 poems has a *Take 5!* mini-lesson with picture book pairings. Matrixes highlight social studies and language arts connections.

Student Edition (K-8)
This companion volume for children features illustrations (no mini-lessons). Listen to 35 poems in Spanish & English—FREE at SoundCloud.com!

"A bubbly and educational bilingual poetry anthology for children." —*Kirkus*

The Poetry Friday Anthology for Science
NSTA Recommends
Featured on ScienceFriday.com + in a monthly column in *Science & Children*
250+ poems on science, technology, engineering, and math

K-5 Teacher/Librarian Edition (K-5)
Each poem is accompanied by a *Take 5!* mini-lesson with both language arts and science-themed teaching tips.

Student Edition (K-8)
The Poetry of Science is an illustrated companion volume for children that is organized by topic and features illustrations (no mini-lessons).

"A treasury of the greatest science poetry for children ever written, with a twist" —NSTA Recommends

Common Core   TEKS

The Poetry Friday Anthology (K-5 Teacher Edition)
A Children's Poet Laureate Pick of the List
36 poems per grade level (K-5) on a wide variety of themes, with *Take 5!* mini-lessons that highlight poetry skills and standards.

The Poetry Friday Anthology for Middle School (Grades 6-8 Teacher Edition)
An NCTE Poetry Notable
36 poems per grade level (grades 6-8) on a wide variety of themes, with *Take 5!* mini-lessons that highlight poetry skills and standards.

Available in a Common Core version or a TEKS version

TEACH READING AND WRITING
WITH THE POETRY FRIDAY POWER BOOK SERIES!

You Just Wait: A Poetry Friday Power Book
(Grades 5 and up)
An NCTE Poetry Notable

This interactive story in poems and writing journal centers around identity, diversity, movies, and sports (soccer and basketball). Extensive back matter resources for readers and writers.

"This delightful collection . . . makes both reading and writing poetry personal and accessible to even the most resistant."
—School Library Journal

Here We Go: A Poetry Friday Power Book
(Grades 3 and up)
An NCTE Poetry Notable
An NNSTOY Social Justice Book

This interactive story inspires kids with themes of diversity and social activism (organizing a walkathon, canned food drive, and school garden). Extensive back matter resources for young writers and kids who want to change the world.

"Filled with poems by a variety of award-winning poets, this engaging resource invites readers to 'power up' and explore the world of poetry."—*Literacy Daily*

Pet Crazy: A Poetry Friday Power Book
(Grades K-4)
A CBC Hot Off the Press selection

This interactive story—with Hidden Language Skills that engage kids in "playing" with punctuation, spelling, and other basics—features three characters who love spending time with animals. Extensive back matter features resources for helping young people perform, read, write, and try to publish poetry.

"An enthusiastic invitation for kids to celebrate their animal friends through poetry composition."—*Kirkus*

FIND SAMPLE POEMS AT PINTEREST.COM/POMELOBOOKS
& AT POMELOBOOKS.COM

Made in the USA
Columbia, SC
27 July 2018